Strategic Materials

IN HEMISPHERE DEFENSE

Strategic Materials

IN HEMISPHERE DEFENSE

by M. S. Hessel, W. J. Murphy, and F. A. Hessel

With a section on Petroleum

by Harold J. Wasson

HASTINGS HOUSE · PUBLISHERS

NEW YORK

ACKNOWLEDGMENT

The authors take this occasion to thank all the friends who were good enough to read individual chapters of this book and who made a great many valuable suggestions. Because of the wish of some of them to remain anonymous, we feel it is better not to name any of these experts although we wish to make public acknowledgment of their generous cooperation.

Thanks are also due to Graham Bretzger, who made the illustrations.

Preface

ONE OF THE first acts of the German Government after September 1939 was to confiscate all privately owned tires in the Reich. The German people, in other words, found out immediately what total war meant for civilians. Americans are just beginning to learn that lesson. Gas and sugar rationing, now, and intimations of fuel oil reductions, next winter, have come as a shock to many of us but we still have our cars and our way of living has been modified but not drastically changed—as yet.

It may be possible for the inevitable changes to come so gradually that we will not be aware of their extent and gravity until we have adjusted ourselves to the new conditions. But it is also possible that a sudden emergency may arise which will require such tremendous quantities of all the instruments of warfare that the people in this country will have to wake up with a jolt to the realization that to win this war absolutely everyone will have to sacrifice both conveniences and comforts.

A war machine such as we must produce to defeat the Axis cannot be achieved by halfway measures. All our resources, and those of our near neighbors, must be used to the fullest extent and enormous as they are they will not stretch far enough to cover civilian needs as well as those of the armed forces.

To keep the Western Hemisphere free from aggression will take the combined good will, energy and natural wealth of all the nations in that hemisphere. They can all help each other; they all need each other. North American industry needs South American raw materials and South America needs our finished products as well as financial assistance.

Way back in the happy days of 1940, when this book was conceived, people were still talking about "beating the Japs in an afternoon" and the question of hemisphere defense seemed pleasantly remote.

We were convinced, however, that the latter was a matter which could quite suddenly become immediate and pressing so that we felt it would be worth while to make a study of the natural resources of the Western Hemisphere as a whole with special emphasis on the raw materials vital to a war effort.

Since we knew that the United States contained ample supplies of so many of these, the logical subjects for research were those substances necessary for war which had to be imported in whole or in part—that is to say—those materials classed as strategic or critical by the Army-Navy Procurement Boards.

The possibilities of obtaining these materials from other countries in the Western Hemisphere would determine the degree to which this country could be independent of the rest of the world, and in a position to defend this hemisphere against any Power or combination of Powers.

So, in the prehistoric days of 1940 we took the Army-Navy lists of strategic and critical raw materials as our guide, believing they would tell the whole story of what this country's procurement problems would be in case of war.

It was not long, however, before we discovered that these carefully compiled lists were woefully incomplete—like a great many other calculations based on that Lilliputian struggle of 25 years ago we used to call a world war.

We were by no means the first to make this discovery; fortunately for this country and for our allies, officials in Washington were aware of the new problems we would have to face long before the general public was conscious of the dangers threatening our security. In fact, as far back as 1939 our Government had begun the accumulation of stock piles of essential materials.

This was not easy to do, for production of civilian goods had to be continued as long as we were not actually at war. Imagine the outcry that would have gone up as late as a year ago if Mr. John Q. Public had been told he could not buy a new car or put new tires on his old one!

Even then, however, manufacturers of essential products were finding it impossible to obtain necessary raw materials. Our giving all-out aid to the democracies had depleted supplies intended for our own defense effort. And products long taken for granted as existing in tremendous quantities were beginning to be scarce or threatening to be so.

That was over a year ago, when 10,000 planes seemed a tremendous number for American industry to produce. Now, the President has announced a program of 60,000 planes, 45,000 tanks, 20,000 anti-aircraft guns and 8 million tons of shipping for 1942, to be practically doubled in 1943. Just try to imagine the amounts of raw materials of all kinds that will be involved in that effort! There just isn't too much of anything any more and most of the things we had always thought of as "coming" to every American are being swallowed up by this giant war machine.

This change from a semi-peace time economy to full war production has meant additional study of strategic raw materials. For this country now faces shortages not only in products normally imported but in some usually produced on such a large scale right here at home as to threaten at times to be a drug on the market. And other materials produced in tremendous quantities in certain parts of the country may become difficult to procure elsewhere because of lack of transportation facilities.

That is why this volume, originally intended as a discussion of only those essential materials which we normally import, must now include chapters on copper, zinc, lead, petroleum, chemicals and drying oils.

There are plenty of stories to be told about the difficulties being encountered by American industry today as it tries to meet the unprecedented demands being made upon it. Blueprints for plant expansion that seemed adequate before December 7, 1941, are now condemned by Government experts as far too small; stock piles, which looked very reassuring on paper, never materialized because the tons of metal to be stored have had to be released to meet the needs of manufacturers of planes, tanks or battleships.

But now Mr. John Q. Public is willing to do without a new car because he is eager to see our fighting forces adequately and speedily equipped to assure us victory; and he has some idea—if a very vague one—of the following facts:

For every 24 autos we are not making this year we have saved steel and rubber for a single 27-ton Medium Tank.

For each automobile we are not making this year we have saved enough tin to coat 1,000 cans in which to put food for our soldiers and sailors.

For every 700 automobiles we are not making this year we have saved enough aluminum—used in pistons and miscellaneous parts— to make one Fighter Plane.

For each automobile we are not making this year we have saved enough nickel to make 100 pounds of nickel steel for Armor Plate, Projectiles, and Armor-Piercing Bullets.

For each automobile we are not making this year we have saved enough zinc and copper to make brass for 2,400 brass Cartridge Cases for the .30 caliber ammunition used in our machine-guns and our Garand semiautomatic rifles and our Springfields.

John Q., Jr., may have less notion of why he can't find a shiny new "juke box" everywhere he goes to buy a soda, but he would be glad to do without the latest tunes if he did know why:

A single one of the larger juke boxes contains enough brass to make 750 Cartridge Cases.

The aluminum in 125 of the bigger juke boxes would make one Fighter Plane.

The steel in one large juke box totals 130 pounds, which would make five Light Machine-guns.

There is no doubt in any one's mind now that machine guns and fighter planes are more vital than juke boxes or automobiles, though it took Pearl Harbor to convince some people. Since that day the change in the average American's point of view has been tremendous, the speed-up in American industry phenomenal. In fact, watching this country go farward for total war has been like turning the crank of a movie projector ever faster and faster. In order to understand the picture, however, we must stop turning for just a moment and take a good look at the actors and their situation.

We find the world divided into two armed camps, with this hemi-sphere and the British Empire the principal occupants of one of them. Let us consider the advantages on "our side." They are tre-mendous as long as the British navy and our own command the seven seas; still considerable if we are forced to depend entirely on the Western Hemisphere for our supplies.

Take, first, what the United States and Britain still control in the way of raw materials—for raw materials are, after all, the *raison d'être* of this whole miserable affair; especially the minerals upon which modern industry is so dependent.

Most of them are to be found only in those regions of the earth that are very far from the industrial centers of the world. That is why it is infinitely more important for the Axis to gain colonies in the East than to win victories in Europe. It is not England which is at stake, but that Empire upon which the sun never sets.

Covering more than one-quarter of the world's surface, the British Commonwealth of Nations contained—while it controlled Malaya and the British East Indies—90 percent of the world's nickel, 70 percent of its chromium, 50 percent of the tin, 40 percent of the manganese, 20 percent of the platinum, 10 percent of the tungsten and nearly all the high-grade mica. In other words, a large percentage of the materials required to make alloy steels, the life-blood of armaments, was in British hands. Half of the wool is produced by Britons, and nearly half of the lead.

Until the Japanese gained control of British and Dutch possessions in the Far East, Britain and her ally, Holland, also produced a substantial part of three other vital raw materials. Nearly one-half of the world's supply of rubber came from British possessions in Malaya and the Malay Archipelago; most of the other half came from the Dutch East India—where nearly all the cinchona bark in the world was also produced.

But control of raw materials by Britain presupposed mastery of the trade routes, and once these were threatened it became apparent how tenuous were the life-lines of an Empire, how fortunate we were in possessing great natural wealth within our own borders.

Over 80 percent of the world output of sulfur and molybdenum, over 80 percent of the petroleum, more than 40 percent of the cotton, steel and iron, 37 percent of the copper, over 20 percent of the aluminum, lead, phosphates, coal and zinc are produced in this country. Russia alone produces more wheat, only that country and Australia more wool, and only France more bauxite.

Moreover, except for purely tropical commodities (rubber, bananas, cocoa, coffee and tea, cork and kapok) and a few minerals we enjoy a unique superabundance not only in all the essential industrial raw materials but also in foods. And most of those we do not possess can be procured from countries near at hand.

In other words, Canada, storehouse of the nickel, platinum and asbestos we lack, and Latin America, where rubber, tin, other minerals and tropical foods can be obtained, offer us far more security than any of England's wide-spread colonies can bring to the British Isles now.

Besides this happy geographical situation, we have the equally important advantage of having the largest industrial output in the world. Thanks to our mass production—so lately maligned by theorists and pseudo-economists—we are equipped as no other nation to assume the title of "arsenal of democracy."

It is we who, for many years, have been consuming over 60 percent of the world's supply of asbestos, molybdenum, petroleum, platinum, silk, sulfur, rubber, vanadium; over 40 percent of the aluminum, coal, copper, chromite, camphor, iron, nickel, mica, sisal and tin; over 20 percent of the antimony, bauxite, coffee, cotton, jute, manila hemp, lead, manganese, mercury, phosphates, sugar, tungsten and zinc.

And out of these raw materials we have been making about one-half of the world's supply of finished industrial products. Germany has put out more planes but we, in producing millions of cars, have built up a manufacturing technique unequaled anywhere in the world.

However, those few raw materials we do lack are so vital to our whole industrial structure that without them it would be greatly weakened and an armament program would be impossible. We could not make one ton of steel, for instance, without manganese nor any of the alloys we need for planes and tanks without nickel and chrome; high-speed tool steels would be impossible without tungsten, to say nothing of what we would do without tin, rubber and the essential fibers.

That is to say, that while we have much to be thankful for, our resources are not inexhaustible and it is going to take careful planning and rationing of certain essentials to turn out the enormous quantities of machines and munitions it will take to defeat Hitler.

We are immeasurably stronger than we were during the last war—when there were about 200 commodities which at one time or another became critically scarce—and this is due principally to the progress of our chemical industry. Were American chemists not prepared to produce synthetic substitutes for such essentials as rubber and silk we could never hope to become self-sufficient.

Those substances for which our chemists will have to provide substitutes are among the materials called strategic. That is to say, they are among those essential to national defense for which, for the duration of this war, we have to depend, in whole or in substantial part, on sources outside the continental limits of the United States and for which strict conservation and distribution control measures are necessary.

According to the *Army-Navy Journal* there are fourteen such materials, nine of them minerals (antimony, chrome, manganese, mercury, mica, nickel, tin, tungsten and quartz crystal), of which four are used directly in the production of steel.

The non-metals on the strategic list are coconut-shell char for gas masks, manila fiber for marine cordage, quinine, rubber and silk—all of vital importance to our armed forces.

Then we come to the critical materials, i.e., those essential to national defense for which the procurement problem in time of war will be less difficult than for those on the strategic list—either because they are less necessary or because they are obtainable in more adequate quantities from domestic sources. For these, less drastic measures of conservation and control are required.

There are fifteen of these, including five minerals (aluminum, asbestos, graphite, platinum and vanadium), some of which are needed for steel; two chemicals necessary in the production of explosives (phenol and toluol); two medicinals (opium and iodine); optical glass, also essential in hospitals as well as for bombsights; two materials needed by the Navy for life-saving equipment (kapok and cork); hides and tanning materials for the making of leather equipment; and wool for clothing.

In other words, the great majority of the essential materials which we do not produce in sufficient quantities for "total" war are minerals which, with rubber, happen to be the very substances without which we would be most seriously embarrassed in the present emergency.

This is because most of these minerals are required to produce what it takes to make war today—tons and tons and then some more tons of steel. We have plenty of iron, coal and limestone to make pig iron, the "first draft" of steel, but we cannot produce (under normal circumstances) enough manganese to make the finished product, nor sufficient quantities of any of the minor metals that go into the various alloy steels so necessary for armaments.

Even for our peacetime requirements during the last five years we have produced only 5 to 6 percent of the manganese, 1 percent of the chromium, 40 percent of the mercury, half of the tungsten, and 10 percent of the antimony we need.

Our total imports of minerals in 1937 were one-sixth of the total value of all our imports, and a large percentage of that one-sixth was composed of minerals on the strategic list.

Available quantities of the other minerals are to be found in many separate and widely distributed areas and their deposits vary in size, grade and accessibility. Most of them, however, are of such low grade that they cannot be worked at a profit except at much higher than normal prices.

This is especially true of antimony, mercury, mica and tungsten, of which our domestic deposits are sufficient in quantity but extremely low in grade. At a price these minerals could be produced in amounts large enough to take care of our emergency needs. Fortunately, the quantities required are small, since it takes but a very little of each one of them to produce products of the desired character. And for two of them, antimony and mercury, adequate substitutes can be had in sufficient quantity to make their procurement not so essential.

Nickel would offer a very serious problem were it not present in large quantities in Canada; and it is fortunate for us that platinum also can be obtained from Canada.

Figures throughout this book are from the Department of Commerce and the Bureau of Mines, and are the latest available. Estimates today are really only glorified guesses, for statistics later than 1940 are in many cases military secrets.

The foods we import are not discussed, inasmuch as not one of them appears on the two Army-Navy lists. This fact is of tremendous importance, of far greater significance, indeed, than can be realized by Americans, so used to having all and more than they need to eat. Our ability to sustain both civilian and armed forces on an adequate diet is one of our greatest advantages today; for a nation which cannot feed its population from within must expend a considerable amount of military effort merely to maintain communications with foreign food-supplying regions.

Moreover, though Russia contains manganese which we lack, and Italy mercury, and though Japan is for the moment in control of the world's greatest source of rubber and tin, the combined possessions of Japan and all the European continental powers do not equal North America in mineral wealth; and the Western Hemisphere is capable of producing nearly every one of the materials essential to national defense.

Given whole-hearted support by Latin America we will have few long-term procurement problems. Alone, we can still manage for a few years' emergency by rigid control and sacrifices on the part of civilians.

Contents

PART III: Additional Materials

PART I

Strategic and Critical Materials

[1]

Pearls of Great Price Lost in the Far East

Rubber and Tin

BEFORE the Japanese victories in Malaya and Java, rubber and tin ranked high on the list of strategic materials, but they did not offer a more serious problem than any one of several other wartime essentials. Since the occupation of the East Indies by our enemies these two products have become super-strategic, as they would say in Hollywood. Tin can be had in modest quantities from South America; rubber is practically unobtainable except from stores already in the country.

Of the two, rubber not only is going to be missed more by Mr. John Q. Public, but also is the more necessary to our arms program. Mechanized equipment absolutely requires rubber, not alone for tires but in a variety of ways, including transmission wires, gas feed lines, etc. The tank not equipped with rubber treads is said to have lost some ten to twenty per cent of its over-all efficiency. Shall we joyride on Sunday and send our boys out to fight and die with less efficient equipment simply because we will not change the normal course of American standards of living? Give the citizens the real facts—they can "take it"—and they will react favorably. But let us not try to bamboozle them with varying degrees of pure hocum!

You and I very probably must get along without new tires for the duration—to say nothing about replacement of any of the thousand and one rubber products we have always taken for granted, from rubber bands to elastic girdles.

Dependent as we are upon cars, we are going to feel the tire shortage most of all, and the cry that was once used to mock the owners of "horseless carriages" may soon be a form of wishful thinking. We

3

will long for horses as we once yearned for the newest thing in streamlined models.

And in snowy weather if we have to walk to work, or to church or school or shop, the fact that we cannot buy a new pair of rubbers or galoshes may be just as much of a shock as the first intimation that we could not get any more tires.

In fact, there are so many ways in which the civilian is going to miss rubber that it would be quite impossible to enumerate them. The Japanese occupation of Java and Malaya is certainly going to revolutionize life *à l'Américaine;* for it will be several years before synthetic rubber production can reach the point where civilian needs can be satisfied.

Daddy is going to have to walk when he needs something at the corner drugstore and Mother is going to have to make soup herself, bake her own beans and preserve her fruit.

Instead of tin cans we will be producing guns and tanks, propeller shafts and torpedo tubes. Tin is not a primary necessity for any of these, but what tin we have will be used for military equipment.

We will receive increasing amounts of tin and some rubber from South America, but not nearly enough for our military needs, much less for civilian uses, for several years to come. Thus for the duration of the war these two materials are bound to be the *bêtes noires* of the military Procurement Divisions, and vanishing quantities for the civilian.

Rubber

War in the Far East was far less interesting to the average American than the baseball scores, when Manchuria, Nanking, Canton, or even Hong Kong was at stake. But the Japanese occupation of Malaya and Java has been a matter of vital concern to everyone in this country. We have all suddenly realized that the tons and tons of rubber consumed in the United States came almost entirely from those far-distant lands, and that as long as they remain in enemy hands we can get no more shipments of that absolutely essential raw material from the East Indies.

And just to make us feel worse comes the mocking thought that the Hevea and Castilloa rubber trees are natives of the western hemisphere and could just as well have been cultivated in many South American and Central American countries as in the Far East. Before 1910 nearly all the rubber used came from the Amazon Valley, where Hevea trees first grew.

The Indians in that part of the world had been using latex from these trees to make water-bottles and bouncing balls, and to protect their feet from cuts and bruises, for many centuries before white men even knew of its existence; and then it took them a long time to make any use of it.

It was Columbus who first brought hardened latex to the notice of Europeans, when he carried home some samples of caoutchouc from his second voyage in 1496. Not until 1770, however, was any use found for this curious substance. Priestly, the great English chemist, discovered that it would remove lead-pencil marks, and named it "rubber." When the eraser became an object of commerce it appeared on the market as the "Indian rubber."

More than a half-century passed. Then in 1832 another chemist, this time a Scot, Charles Macintosh, found that cloth impregnated with rubber was waterproof and so invented the "macintosh," still indispensable to every British wardrobe. The first of these coats, however, were sticky in summer and stiff in winter because the Scot's process did not in any way render the material resistant to changes of temperature.

It took an American, Charles Goodyear, to make this possible and his invention of the process of vulcanization (by the addition of sulfur) in 1839, marks the real beginning of the rubber industry.

After Goodyear's discovery rubber became increasingly important, and Great Britain had the vision to realize how lucrative the production of rubber might be if the Brazilian tree could be grown in Ceylon and Malaya. The Royal Gardens at Kew sent Henry A. Wickham on an expedition to the Amazon Valley to get seeds of *Hevea brasiliensis,* which Brazil had strictly forbidden to be taken from the country. In 1860 Wickham managed to smuggle some carefully selected seeds past the Brazilian customs and transport them safely to England. They were planted at Kew; and when the seedlings were sturdy enough they were sent to the Botanical Gardens at Ceylon and became the nucleus of plantations which eventually furnished 90 to 95 percent of the world's supply of rubber.

Before 1839 about 10,000 tons of rubber were produced a year; twenty years later this amount had been increased three-fold; and by 1900 54,000 tons were being produced annually.

Then came the discovery by Marks and Oenslager that aniline oil would greatly accelerate the rate of vulcanization, a discovery which both cut the cost of manufacture and improved the quality of rubber products. And, finally, the development in 1914 by American companies of the use of carbon black added tremendously to the efficiency of automobile tires.

With the advent of the automobile, rubber had started on its dizzy upward consumption spiral, and as cars became more and more general the consumption of rubber grew apace. In the past thirty years the annual American needs of rubber increased from 1 to $10\frac{1}{2}$ pounds for every person. In 1941 we consumed over 800,000 tons.

RUBBER
WORLD   PRODUCTION   1941

DUTCH EAST INDIES – BRITISH MALAYA 97%
SOUTH AMERICA 2%
MISCELLANEOUS 1%

Our rubber goods manufacturing industry is the largest in the world; and on the value basis, crude rubber is almost the most important single commodity imported into the United States. 97 percent of it came from the Far East—60 percent from British Malaya and most of the rest from the Netherlands Indies. Normally, about 80 percent of this rubber is used by the automobile industry, 16 percent for hose, belts, druggists' supplies and so forth, and about 4 percent in rubber boots and shoes.

One American manufacturer boasts of making 32,000 different items from rubber, including molded articles, sheet rubber, proofed material, footwear, sponge rubber, tires and tubes, raw rubber goods, latex solution, vulcanite or hard rubber, and dipped goods.

Rubber is indispensable in the manufacture of motor vehicles, airplanes, submarines, balloons, gas masks, electric motors, ships, trains, street-cars, electric lights, telephones, typewriters, printers' tools, wireless apparatus, radios, medical goods, fire and garden hose, tubing of various sorts, milking machines, athletic goods and several types of shoes. And it is used, though not indispensable, in many other commodities.

As for strictly military uses, besides those included in the list above we cannot fail to mention bullet-proof gasoline tanks; de-icers to crack loose the ice that forms on the wings of planes; rubberized flying suits and electrically-heated underwear and boots, and the rubberized suits and boots for fire-fighters; barrage balloons; rubber track blocks for combat vehicles, as well as latex cushions to protect the men inside; flotation bags for use in planes that fly over water, and inflatable rubber boats; truck tires so constructed that they can continue in service for as much as 100 miles even though riddled with bullets, due to inner tubes that close up bullet holes without appreciable loss of air pressure, and self-sealing airplane fuel-line hose that will seal up machine-gun bullet holes; air-foam pads for wounded arms and legs, Goodyear water-proof, transparent Pliofilm bandages, besides all the familiar hospital uses for rubber—water-bottles, ice-packs, surgeon's gloves and so forth.

Obviously, modern warfare could not be waged without rubber. And we do not produce an ounce of it aside from a very small amount from guayule plantations in the Southwest. What can we do now that it has become impossible to receive shipments from the Far East?

The first thing we can do and are doing, is to stimulate the production of synthetic rubber, as that alone would enable us to be absolutely independent. The second possibility is to increase our imports from South and Central America, which, after all, are the natural habitats of the most important rubber trees.

Back in 1926 our Government sent specialists to Latin America to investigate the possibilities of producing rubber in the Western Hemisphere. These scientists returned with the information that in more than six million acres in tropical America the physical conditions were favorable to the growth of rubber trees and that the only important hindrance to large plantations was scarcity of labor. This, they suggested, could be remedied by the importation of coolies to those lands having adequate transportation facilities to the seaboard.

We did nothing, however, until all too recently. After the beginning of the present war our Government became, once more, interested in the production of rubber, and $500,000 was appropriated to the Department of Agriculture for a group of American scientists to co-operate with the authorities of Central and South American countries in the development of a Western Hemisphere rubber supply.

So far, we have seen only one report—that of Llewellyn Williams, curator of the Economic Botany Department of the Field Museum, Chicago, who stated that wild rubber trees were growing abundantly under ideal conditions over an area of 40,000 square miles in the virtually unexplored Orinoco Valley of Venezuela—adjacent to all the water routes leading to American processing plants.

Unfortunately, the largest amount of rubber that has yet been produced in South America was 49,000 long tons in 1912; and in 1930 only 16,000 tons came from there. Nearly all the rubber produced has been from wild trees; cultivation has been negligible due to the South American leaf disease.

Since it requires some time to clear the jungle forest and prepare the land for planting rubber trees, and then more than five years for the trees to reach the bearing stage, a thriving rubber industry cannot be produced on short notice. According to E. G. Holt, Chief, Consumption Materials Unit, Bureau of Foreign and Domestic Commerce, it would take a dozen or more years to supply an appreciable percentage of needs from new plantations.

Luckily for us, the Ford Motor Company several years ago started planting Hevea trees in the State of Pará, Brazil, and their plantations, under the guidance of experts, have already reached the producing stage. Also, the Brazilian Government has been planting in Pará and in the State of Amazonas. Another large American tire manufacturer has been planting rubber trees in Costa Rica on a large acreage and these trees are now nearly three years old.

Bolivia and Peru contain ideal rubber country which eventually could be made to produce substantial quantities of this material; but we cannot count on any large amount from them for several years, even though we have started to encourage the cultivation of rubber trees in those countries.

In Mexico there has always been a small amount of rubber produced from guayule, the desert shrub, which also grows in our Southwest, but the largest figures, those for 1921, were only 10,000 long tons; and in 1938 only 3,000 long tons were produced.

As for 1940, E. G. Holt states the situation clearly: "If the entire rubber output of Latin America and Africa last year had come to the United States—and it did not—it would not have kept our industry going three weeks."

Consequently, it does not seem likely that we can count on any significant supply of rubber from either South or Central America within the next two or three years, at least—and they will be the crucial years.

It had been estimated before this war that we would need 200,000 long tons of crude rubber for military purposes alone, over a two-year period of emergency, and 1,000,000 long tons for civilian needs; while our domestic resources then amounted to the following:

	LONG TONS
Stocks of crude rubber on hand	335,000
Stocks of reclaimed rubber on hand	20,000
Estimated available stocks afloat	15,000
Secondary recovery from scraps	400,000
	770,000

In June, 1939, this Government began to build up stock piles of rubber and made an agreement with the British Government to exchange 600,000 bales of cotton for 85,000 tons of rubber—all of which had been received by November, 1940.

That was only the beginning, however. In July, 1940, the RFC formed the Rubber Reserve Company for the purpose of acquiring rubber reserves to raise our stock piles to 415,000 tons. By August 31, 1941, these amounted to only 228,551 tons.

General import figures for the first eleven months of 1940, however, showed net imports of 712,000 tons, and approximate consumption 610,000 tons. The total stocks in this country in September, 1941, were about 450,000 tons, with a consumption of 50,000 to 70,000 tons a month.

There is reason to believe that our stocks on January 1, 1942, amounted to about 600,000 tons, possibly even more, although this is not officially admitted.

The drastic tire regulation is the direct consequence of the extremely dangerous position we now find ourselves in with respect to rubber. Increased treading of old casings is possible, and steps have been taken to reclaim larger supplies of scrap, which would double the present output of 170,000 tons of rubber so produced; motorless week-ends —at least in the Eastern Seaboard States through the medium of gasoline rationing, and speed laws are already being drastically enforced— cutting consumption in tires by one-third.

When the war broke out in 1939, the German Government confiscated the tires on every private car at once. That may never be necessary here, but if the war is long—?

We shall certainly have to take drastic measures to tide us over until production of synthetic rubber can be sufficiently increased to meet our needs. So let us see what the American chemists have produced to take the place of natural rubber.

To begin with, there are two general definitions of synthetic rubber. First: "An organic material may be called a rubber when it shows a high elasticity of 100 percent or more at room temperature, and when it does not lose this property upon storage at room temperature during considerable periods." Second: "Synthetic rubbers are those organic substances which possess the property of forcibly retracting to approximately their original size and shape after being distorted."

In other words, rubber has not been really synthesized, as indigo has been, but substances have been produced which have the properties of natural rubber.

The first of these was isoprene, recognized as the mother-substance of caoutchouc and capable of polymerization into a rubberlike substance. Before the First World War serious efforts were made to find ways of producing isoprene commercially, but no one was ever successful in making a product which could be compared to natural rubber.

During that war, however, the Germans were so hard pressed for the natural product that their chemists, by a veritable *tour de force*, managed to produce synthetic rubber from methyl butadiene, one of the coal-tar derivatives, of which Germany had ample supplies. This substitute was far from perfect, but infinitely better than isoprene.

After the war, when free trade was resumed again, the search for synthetic rubber was practically abandoned until 1925, when high prices led to another intensive campaign to produce a rubber substitute.

This time chloroprene was discovered. It more closely resembled vulcanized rubber in its elastic properties than any previous synthetic product. As a matter of fact, chloroprene was preferable to natural rubber in some respects.

Some years later thiokol was developed in this country quite accidentally by J. C. Patrick in an effort really directed at making an antifreeze solution. Thiokol is made from salt, natural gas and sulfur. Over one million pounds of this substance were used in 1938 for gaskets, gasoline hose, paint-spray hose and so forth. It holds considerable possibilities for producing retreads but most certainly output is not sufficient to give civilians much, if any, hope.

Very soon after the discovery of thiokol came the development of neoprene, which is made by the polymerization of chloroprene. Besides being oil-resistant, it does not react to sunlight, oxidation, heat and many chemicals. The basic chemistry for this development was supplied by the pure research on acetylene and its compounds by the late Father Niewlands, of Notre Dame University. The physical properties of neoprene closely resemble those of vulcanized rubber, and the synthetic product, after vulcanization, has substantially the same tensile strength, ultimate elongation and elasticity as natural, vulcanized rubber.

Synthetic rubbers are more expensive than the natural product in normal times, and can be sold only to consumers to whom their technical value justifies a higher cost. This value is very considerable, however, in certain cases, such as elastic rings for industrial equipment used to prevent the passage of gases or liquids into moving parts; the corona-proof sheath for high-tension power cables, and automobile ignition cables; hose for conveying crude and refined petroleum; aprons, gloves and other protective garments. Also, neoprene is 20 percent more efficient than natural rubber for high-grade rubber tread tires.

Just a year after the development of neoprene Goodrich put a synthetic rubber on the market—koroseal.

Next came buna, made from butadiene (a product of cracked gas or petroleum gases) and used either by itself or coreacted with various other organic compounds, such as styrene, etc. This is the synthetic rubber now supplying 75 percent of Germany's needs. Standard Oil of New Jersey had the exclusive patent rights to produce buna in this country and had granted a license to the Firestone Tire and Rubber Company. Now, by order of the government this license has been extended to other companies who are building plants for the manufacture of the buna rubber.

Buna (commonly referred to as Buna S) resists abrasion better than natural rubber; and perbunan (commonly referred to as Buna N), the product of the polymerization of butadiene and acrylonitrile (a combination of a product of cracking gas and nitrogen) has this same quality, as well as being more resistant to heat, age and the deteriorating effects of oil and acid. In fact, road tests on passenger car tires have shown the butadiene-styrene interpolymers, neoprene, and the butadiene-acrylonitrile interpolymers to be equal to natural rubber in tread wear. This means that, though rubber manufacturers might have to modify their equipment or processing techniques in order to use these synthetic rubbers in tires, we would not be seriously handicapped from the standpoint of quality by the introduction of synthetic rubbers in passenger car tire treads. Moreover, truck tire treads made from certain of these synthetic rubbers are said to be definitely superior to natural rubber compounds under unusually severe conditions of service.

Butyl type rubber, developed by chemists of the Standard Oil Company of New Jersey, offers extremely interesting possibilities, yet it is still very much in the development stages and much must yet be learned concerning its properties. It is cheaper to produce than the Buna types but for tires is not as satisfactory, at least at the present moment.

The reason these synthetics have not heretofore been produced on a very large scale is because it is hard to compete, economically, with natural rubber. Just consider the thrifty *Hevea brasiliensis* from which 98 percent of the world's rubber comes. It draws carbon from the air in the form of carbon dioxide, hydrogen from the soil in the form of water, provides its own catalysts and uses the heat of the sun to "do the trick." Consequently, the average total cost of rubber in the East is 5 cents a pound (excluding return on investment) and the average plantation produces 400 pounds per acre.

Cheap as it is, however, natural rubber has definite disadvantages, of which the foremost is its lack of uniformity. Synthetic rubber, on the other hand, can be perfectly uniform, its properties controlled by its chemical composition. These properties include abrasion resistance to offset natural rubber's inability to stand long wear; resistance to oxidation to offset natural rubber's tendency to react to atmospheric conditions; strength to resist forces that fatigue and distort the shape of natural rubber; resistance to chemicals to offset the latter's tendency to deteriorate rapidly under the influence of many chemicals, especially animal, vegetable and mineral oils.

Consequently, at a time such as this, when cost becomes a matter of secondary importance, synthetic rubber can easily replace the natural substance—provided we can produce enough of it!

Until the present emergency arose synthetics were being developed primarily to produce more satisfactory rubber for certain specialties consuming a limited amount; now they are needed for the tires and tubes which consume about 75 percent of the crude rubber used in this country. This means that overnight the demand for synthetic rubber has changed from that of moderate-scale operation to one of tremendous magnitude. Production capacity, which was geared to take care of 1 percent of our crude rubber requirements, had to be speeded up to meet all our needs as soon as possible.

Although the polysulfide rubbers and the flexible, non-vulcanizable plastics could be substituted for rubber in many of its industrial applications, nevertheless there are important industrial uses for rubber in which the requirements are much the same as for tire treads, and hence the only available substitutes for the natural product are the butadiene rubbers and the neoprenes. This is true of such important tonnage consumers of crude rubber as power transmission and conveyor belts, engine mountings, and, in general, products that are subjected in service to severe mechanical stresses or to high temperatures. Hence our principal problem is to supply adequate quantities of the synthetic rubbers.

The American rubber companies have met this challenge with unprecedented efficiency and resourcefulness. Just take the record for 1940: (1) DuPont spent over $2,000,000 to increase the production facilities for making neoprene to a capacity of 1,000,000 pounds a month, to be raised to 1,500,000 pounds. (2) Standard Oil of New Jersey acquired control of the I. G. Farben's American patents on buna and made public their plan to build a plant at Baton Rouge with a capacity of 10,000 pounds a day. (3) Goodrich and Phillips Petroleum formed a new organization, the Hydrocarbon Chemical and Rubber Company, with a plant having an initial capacity of 2000 tons a year of Hycar, of which there are two grades—one for tires, the other for oil-resistant applications. (4) Goodrich also announced an increase in the production of Ameripol. (5) American Cyanamid announced that the output of acrylonitrile had been doubled.

But in 1941 we produced approximately 12,000 tons of synthetic rubber and in the light of the swift developments in the Far East in the fall of that year and the first few months of the present year such an amount became hopelessly inadequate and a stupendous plan of production of synthetic rubbers was finally undertaken not without great confusion and clashes of conflicting factions. Tragically rubber literally became a political football of the first order.

One of the serious "bottlenecks" in the synthetic rubber program is steel. It takes one and one-quarter tons of steel for every ton of synthetic rubber capacity. On the basis of a program of 800,000 tons of rubber annually this means one million tons of steel for construction of the plants.

Indicative of the urgency of the situation is the fact that in January of this year the synthetic rubber program then formulated called for 400,000 long tons. In April this figure was increased to 800,000 long tons and is to consist of 700,000 tons of general purpose rubber, largely of Buna types, 60,000 tons of Butyl and 30,000 tons of neoprene, plus an increased amount of thiokol.

Synthetic rubber can be produced from almost any material that is a hydrocarbon in nature, but the petroleum industry will supply the largest portion of the necessary butadiene.

This decision immediately caused the "farm chemurgists" to raise terrific objections, asserting that the oil interests were unduly influencing the plans of the War Production Board and that alcohol made from grains (principally corn) should be utilized as the raw material for the manufacture of butadiene.

By converting the distilling industry largely over to production of industrial alcohol several million gallons of that material will be made available for supplying butadiene despite the fact that alcohol is vitally necessary in the manufacture of explosives. Thus in part at least our synthetic rubber will come from alcohol but the overwhelming portion under present plans will be derived from petroleum.

Those who oppose the plan of the "farm chemurgists" point out that rubber made from synthetic alcohol is considerably cheaper than rubber produced from alcohol derived from corn and that the "chemurgists" are merely attempting to capitalize on the present emergency

to obtain government funds to erect alcohol plants in the grain producing states of the Midwest which will be available in the post-war
period for the manufacture of alcohol-gasoline fuel blends.

Opponents of the proposal to make synthetic rubber from alcohol
produced from grain also point out the scarcity of necessary materials
and equipment to erect alcohol plants in the "middle of the cornfields
of America."

The "chemurgists," on the other hand, insist that the contention
that materials of construction would be a hopeless bottleneck is but
a smokescreen—that only glass, porcelain, a little copper or silver

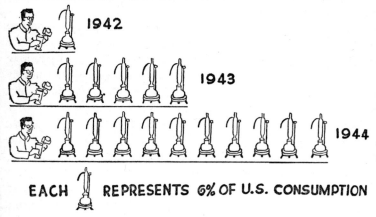

SYNTHETIC RUBBER

ANTICIPATED UNITED STATES PRODUCTION —

1942

1943

1944

EACH REPRESENTS 6% OF U.S. CONSUMPTION

plus wood for the fermentation vats are necessary for the construction
of the one hundred alcohol plants that they would erect, each turning
out 45,000 pounds of butadiene daily from some types of corn. William
J. Hale, "father of chemurgy," insists that rubber can probably be
produced for 15 cents a pound from waxy maize and grain sorghums,
and, further, that one hundred and fifty million bushels of corn will
produce all the rubber we can possibly use and that such a quantity
represents less than five percent of our crop.

All these conflicting statements leave the average non-technically
brained citizen bewildered and perplexed. John Q. Public one day is
assured that he is likely to have rubber tires in the not too distant

future while in the next twenty-four hours he is warned that he not only will not have new tires for the duration but may find that Uncle Sam probably will take away those now on the family jallopy.

But John Q. Public will find that whether synthetic rubber is made from petroleum or alcohol (made either synthetically or from grain) that he will not share in any such production for at least three years for the very good and simple reason that whatever amounts are made in that period will be taken for the war machines of the United Nations.

The entire situation is further complicated by those who insist that as much as ten million tons of rubber can be obtained from the scrap piles of the United States but import figures fail to substantiate any such claims, for total imports from 1839 to 1940 are said to total not more than twelve million tons. A rubber tire is in fact a combination of rubber, cotton and a wide variety of chemicals. Indeed the average tire contains approximately but ten pounds of rubber. The longer tires are used the less rubber is available for reclaim. No wonder our government is concerned about the thirty million cars and trucks on the highways of America, for they constitute our most valuable possession today in the all-out fight for survival.

TABLE I

American Synthetic Rubber Production [a]
(Long Tons)

	NEOPRENE TYPES	BUTADIENE TYPES	POLYSULFIDE TYPES	TOTAL
1939	1750	None	500	2,250
1940	2500	60	700	3,260
1941 (estimate)	6300	4000	1400	11,700

TABLE II

	NATURAL	THIOKOL	NEOPRENE	BUNA
Cost per cubic foot [b]	$11.28	$38.60	$50.40	$51.90
Strength	High	Low	High	High [c]
Elasticity	High	Low	Medium High	Medium
High temperature toughness	Good	Poor	Poor	Poor
Oxygen resistance	Fair	Excellent	Excellent	Excellent
Flexing resistance	Good	Poor	Excellent	Excellent
Handling resistance	Best	Fair to Poor	Fair to Good	Fair to Poor
Resistance to solvents	Poor	Excellent	Good to Exc.	Excellent

TABLE III

Partial Idea of Production Built or Being Built by Various Companies as of end of 1941

PRODUCER	TYPE	PRESENT ANNUAL OUTPUT	TOTAL PLANNED
		Tons	*Tons*
DuPont	Neoprene	6,000	20,000
Goodrich-Phillips	Ameripol	3,600	10,000
Goodyear	Chemigum	5,000	10,000
Standard Oil of New Jersey	Butyl	2,000	
Standard Oil of Louisiana	Buna & Butyl	2,000	15,000
Firestone	Buna		10,000
U. S. Rubber	"		10,000
Shell	"	5,000	
Dow	Thiokol	11,000	20,000

[a] E. R. Bridgewater, Manager, Rubber Chemicals Division, E. I. DuPont.
[b] Based on prices September 12, 1940.
[c] With carbon black.

Crude rubber, Guayule: United States imports for consumption, in specified years, 1929 to 1940

YEAR	QUANTITY (1000 POUNDS)
1929	2,857
1932	———
1936	2,753
1937	6,028
1938	5,618
1939	5,001
1940[a]	8,139

[a] Preliminary.

SOURCE: Compiled from official statistics of the U. S. Department of Commerce.

Milk of rubber, or latex: United States imports for consumption, by principal sources, in specified years, 1929 to 1940

COUNTRY	1929	1932	1936	1937	1938	1939	1940 [a]
	QUANTITY (1,000 POUNDS [b])						
Latin America:							
Brazil	—	—	—	35	34	39	4
Other countries:							
Netherlands Indies	3,196	6,716	20,937	28,687	12,433	30,261	37,908
British Malaya	4,826	3,586	21,103	20,569	11,147	25,778	28,728
Liberia	14	—	1,589	2,548	2,950	5,193	9,047
Ceylon	—	192	10	45	190	88	—
United Kingdom	86	692	815	1	—	1	—
All other	233	264	16	49	[c]	100	—
Total imports	8,355	11,450	44,470	51,934	26,754	61,460	75,687

[a] Preliminary.
[b] Dry rubber content.
[c] Less than 500.

SOURCE: Compiled from official statistics of the U. S. Department of Commerce.

Crude rubber, Hevea, Caucho, and other natural [a]: United States imports for consumption, by principal sources, in specified years, 1929 to 1940

COUNTRY	1929	1932	1936	1937	1938	1939	1940 [b]
	QUANTITY (1,000 POUNDS)						
Latin America:							
Brazil	23,176	5,142	8,972	12,831	7,282	10,480	12,523
Ecuador	593	—	1,211	421	511	1,564	3,058
Bolivia	—	56	166	53	465	543	484
Peru	570	28	946	1,106	530	44	294
All other	297	1	101	308	45	73	122
Total Latin American countries	24,636	5,227	11,396	14,719	8,833	12,704	16,481

[a] Crude rubber, other than latex, guayule, jelutong, and pontianak.
[b] Preliminary.

SOURCE: Compiled from official statistics of the U. S. Department of Commerce.

Crude rubber, Hevea, Caucho, and other natural [a]: United States imports for consumption, 1929 to 1940 (*continued*)

COUNTRY	1929	1932	1936	1937	1938	1939	1940 [b]
			QUANTITY (1,000 POUNDS)				
Other countries:							
British Malaya	891,471	652,033	740,026	844,149	536,787	597,318	914,533
Netherlands Indies	200,136	152,306	194,292	314,486	233,699	290,141	606,368
Ceylon	120,989	67,160	60,462	67,129	55,492	77,904	123,202
French Indo-China	—	101	29,528	36,503	45,254	58,207	64,530
British India (including Burma)	3,332	817	1,932	7,253	4,805	7,548	12,216
United Kingdom	9,777	32,449	4,997	693	695	144	—
All other	4,242	7,313	3,590	3,601	5,149	8,713	11,706
Total imports	1,254,583	917,406	1,046,223	1,288,533	890,714	1,052,679	1,749,036

Crude rubber: Exports from producing countries and regions, in specified years, 1929 to 1938

COUNTRY	1929	1932	1936	1937	1938
		QUANTITY (1,000 LONG TONS)			
Latin America [a]	22.6	6.5	15.9	19.7	18.1
British colonies:					
Malaya, including Brunei and Labuan	457.0	406.0	353.7	469.9	372.0
Ceylon	80.3	49.3	49.7	70.4	49.5
British India	7.9	1.1	8.6	9.8	8.5
Burma	5.5	3.0	5.8	7.2	6.7
North Borneo	7.4	5.4	8.2	13.2	9.5
Sarawak	11.2	7.1	21.0	25.9	17.8
Total British colonies	569.3	471.9	447.0	596.4	464.0
Other countries:					
Netherlands Indies	225.0	211.0	309.6	431.7	298.1
French Indo-China	9.5	13.5	40.8	43.4	59.2
Thailand (Siam)	4.3	3.0	34.6	35.6	41.6
Philippines and Oceania	.9	.8	1.6	1.6	2.0
Liberia	.2	—	1.6	2.3	2.9
Other Africa	6.1	2.0	6.8	9.1	9.0
World total	837.9	708.7	857.9	1,139.8	894.9
		Percent of world total			
Latin America	2.7	0.9	1.9	1.7	2.0

[a] About three-fourths of the crude rubber produced in Latin America is exported from Brazil. Mexico produces guayule rubber.

SOURCE: Statistical Bulletin of the International Rubber Regulation Committee, May, 1940.

Tin

Tin is an ancient metal with a very up-to-date importance. An essential part of the tools and weapons of the Bronze Age, it is a strategic raw material today and one of the principal stakes for which a fierce war is now raging in the Pacific.

The principal ore, cassiterite, which contains 7.8 percent of tin, is widely distributed over the earth's surface; but, like chromium and manganese, it is found in large quantities only in a few countries—all of them far removed from the industrial centers where the metal is consumed.

Most of it comes from the southeast corner of Asia, "where the Malay Peninsula sticks out like a long finger into the Indian Ocean." Large deposits begin in southern Siam and run through the Federated Malay States and the Straits Settlements and then appear again in the Dutch Islands to the south. And then, far across the Pacific and high in the Bolivian Andes, 15,000 feet above the sea, there are other deposits of this metal—not as large as those in East Asia but more extensive than any of the others scattered over the earth.

Normally Bolivia produces 20 percent of the world's supply of tin; Malaya and the Dutch East Indies 75 percent. The lion's share of the world's total supply of tin was thus in the hands of British and Dutch interests; also, a very large percentage of the metal usually passes through British, Malayan and Dutch East Indian smelters before it reaches world markets; 20 percent is smelted in England and some in the Belgian Congo and Australia.

Under these conditions it is small wonder that the Japanese occupation of Malaya and the Dutch East Indies constitutes one of the most serious blows to our life line of vital raw materials yet felt in World War II.

Normally we neither produce nor smelt tin ore on a commercial scale in this country. During the last war the American Smelting and Refining Company and the National Lead Company did run smelters, which have long since been closed. However, the Government, through the RFC, is financing a large smelter to produce 52,000 tons a year mainly from Bolivian concentrates. The latter are to be supplied in accordance with an agreement made with the Bolivian Government for the importation of the 18,000 tons of pure tin every year for the next five years. The smelter plant, being built by the Tin Processing Corporation, a subsidiary of the Dutch N. V. Billiton Maatschappij of Arnheim, was originally planned to have a capacity of 18,000 tons a year, to cost $3,500,000, and to be ready for operation early in 1942. Materials for its completion have been given a priority rating of A-1-A and it is expected to be operating this year at the 52,000-ton capacity.

Bolivian ore cannot be received in sufficient quantity to maintain this rate of production, but there is now a large supply of ore on hand and any change in the fortunes of war may result in concentrates from other areas reaching this country.

The location of the smelter on the seacoast of Texas is convenient for receiving ore from Bolivia, as well as for shipping the metal by sea, and is accessible to plentiful supplies of cheap gas for fuel.

Still in the pilot plant stage are new processes being developed by Phelps Dodge, the American Smelting & Refining Company and the American Metals Corporation which may also add to our smelting capacity.

As for our domestic deposits of tin, there are a few minor ones in Alaska and even smaller ones in the Carolinas, Alabama, Virginia, North Dakota, Texas, California, and Nevada, but the most they have ever produced (in 1910) was 140 tons of tin; in 1940 they yielded exactly 44 tons, and the entire recorded output of the whole North American continent would not satisfy normal domestic consumption for more than one week.

In a great emergency, and only after the eighteen months it would take to build plants and install equipment, we might achieve an annual output of from three to six thousand tons at a high price—and that only for a brief period. We would then be producing less than 8 percent of our normal demand, for we consume about 90,000 short tons of tin a year—nearly half of the world's supply of the metal plus about 20,000 tons recovered in this country from scrap (10 percent of this as a by-product in the manufacture of tin cans).

Over 40 percent of the tin used in this country goes into tinplate and terneplate; for, besides having a low melting-point, this metal has the happy faculty of forming a thin, ductile, noncorrosive and closely adhering film or coating on steel. This coating, often 1/1000 of an inch thick, is applied by dipping thin sheets of steel into a blend of African palm oil and then into the melted tin. The resulting tinplate is non-toxic and ideal for food preservation.

Already we have made notable progress in saving our precious tin stocks. An electrodeposition process has been successfully developed that reduces the amount of tin on the walls of the tin can. Special lacquers and enamels have been found satisfactory for certain linings of containers. The chemist is far from idle!

Terneplate is used for tanks and roofing, due to its high degree of corrosive resistance, while tinplate is used for food containers.

Solder, containing 35 percent lead and 60 percent tin, accounts for over 20 percent of our tin consumption and is extremely useful for automobile radiators and radio sets. Babbitt (8.31 percent tin), ideal for bearings, is also used in automobile engines and in other machines.

The other principal uses of tin are shown in the following table listing the applications of this metal in the order of their importance as consumers:

U. S. Consumption 1938

	New Tin %	Secondary %
Tinplate	41.6	
Solder	22.6	45.6
Babbitt	7.4	11.0
Bronze	7.0	13.8
Collapsible Tubes	6.1	
Chemicals	3.6	11.6
Bar Tin, Tubing & Pipe	2.8	1.8
Type Metal	2.0	8.4
Terneplate	1.8	6.4
Foil	1.5	
Galvanizing	1.4	
Other Alloys	1.4	0.6
Miscellaneous	0.8	0.8
	100.0	100.0

It is evident from the above that since tin is essentially an industrial material, only indirectly connected with the steel industry—through tinplate, solder and bearing alloys—it does not have the same strategic importance as metals like nickel, chromium and tungsten, which are essential in the production of steel itself. That is why a war could be carried on with comparatively small amounts of tin—as was proved by Germany in the First World War.

This does not mean that tin does not have many military uses. The following lists will prove that it has. The first is of army equipment in which tin is used; the second is of navy needs.

Army Equipment

Food containers	Refrigerators
Machine-guns	Cameras
Pistols	Adjustment & deflection boards
Rifles	Height & range finders
Machine-gun mounts	Angle & observation instruments
Projectors	Repair kits
Gun carriages	Sound locators
Wagons	Gun predicators
Smoke screens (tetra-chloride)	Time interval recorders
Cars	Telescopes
Compasses	Tractors
Fuse setters	Helmets
Thermometers	Band instruments
Tanks	Water-bags
Trailers	Buckets
Tripods	Forks, spoons, etc.
Trumpets	Engines
Boilers & covers	Batteries
Dippers	Tachometers

Navy Equipment

Engines	Cables
Bronze for journals	Condenser tubes
Gun mounts	Torpedo tubes
Rods	Valves
Pipes	Food containers
Bomb fuses	Bomb cases
Propeller shafts	Electric connections
Radio condenser casings	Generators
Condenser heads	Radio circuits
Binnacles	Compasses
Smoke screens (tetra-chloride)	

As far as the armed forces are concerned, tin is an extremely useful if not essential raw material, and in some cases it is irreplaceable. In many other cases there are substitutes available. For plating, for instance, porcelain, enamel, steel, can be used, as can synthetic resin on steel, or even plated plastics; and for vacuum cleaners and refrigerators a special tinless graphite bearing is possible. For babbitt metal, in many cases lead babbitt containing no tin will do.

As for food containers, which account for at least 60 percent of our consumption of tin, the substitutes which have been most successfully applied so far, glass and aluminum, may not prove to be entirely sufficient or wholly satisfactory in time of war; glass is too heavy for use in the armed forces and aluminum has more important duties to perform. And any tremendous further expansion in glass and aluminum production will require large tonnages of chemicals (soda ash is one example) that will be difficult to secure under present war-time conditions.

There are other ways of solving the problem, however. Lacquered or cellophane-lined steel is one possibility, and waxed paper cartons such as are now used for milk could serve for vegetables and fruits. But this, in turn, depends on an abundance of properly prepared cellulose, which does not exist. We are very much like the man who could have ham and eggs for breakfast if he only had the ham and the eggs.

Solder can be largely displaced by the use of alloys of lead and silver, cadmium and zinc which have met all tests so far; and the United States Bureau of Standards has perfected alloys which might entirely replace babbitt for bearings. They were being adopted extensively by the automobile industry (the heaviest user of bearing metals) just before that industry folded up in the face of an all-out war production program.

As far as purely civilian needs are concerned, cellophane is already competing with tin for foil, and lead alloys are being increasingly used in tubes; while terneplate could almost entirely be eliminated for roofing, and could be replaced by other materials for tanks, fuel cans and stoppers.

This means that it was very essential that the Government establish strict control over all our available resources of tin. This metal will be replaced in many instances and the amounts normally so consumed will be allocated to the most important military and civilian needs. We shall probably not need more than 70,000 short tons over a two-year period.

Civilian uses of tin have already been curtailed. In December, 1941, the OPM issued an order prohibiting the use of tin after March 31, 1942, on twenty-nine different products, including musical instruments, tinfoil, toys, household furnishings, jewelry, buckles and

TIN
WORLD PRODUCTION 1940

MALAY STATES

NETHERLAND INDIES

SOUTH AMERICA

ASIA

AFRICA

EACH REPRESENTS 10,000 LONG TONS

various novelties, beverage dispensing units, pewter, refrigerator trays, chimes and bells; and an immediate 50 percent reduction in the use of tin for these purposes was ordered at the same time.

While no new restrictions were at that time put on the tin used in the 17,000,000,000 tin-lined cans manufactured annually in this country, a conservation order was later issued limiting their production and use.

Only tin, tin alloys and scrap were affected by the first order, which exempted the type metal used in the printing and publishing trade.

It was estimated by OPM officials that the order would reduce the 1942 demand for tin by some 15,000 tons—a drop in the bucket as compared with those 100,000 tons we used to import every year from Malaya. So we expected to hear a great deal more about restrictions on tin, and it might be added that we have heard plenty.

At the beginning of 1940 consumers' stocks of tin were 15 percent higher than usual and the industrial stocks of virgin pig tin were sufficient for about four months (at the 1939 rate of consumption). Adding to these the tin in transit, afloat or in warehouses, we had total stocks of tin enough for six months—and these did not include government stock piles. We now have stocks for about ten to fourteen months' consumption. Large consumers usually carry from three to six months' stocks, and all industry about three months' supply. Actual scrap recovery is about 26,000 to 30,000 tons.

Our Government has taken very energetic action to assure us tin supplies. First, an expert was appointed to study the situation and make suggestions. Mr. Erwin Vogelsang, formerly president of the New York Metal Exchange and National Metal Exchange, Inc., was appointed consultant on tin to the Advisory Commission to the Council of National Defense.

This appointment was made in June of 1940, and on July 1st of that year an agreement was reached with the International Tin Committee for an increase in tin production enabling this country to buy more of the metal. The United States, in fact, contracted to purchase all surplus tin offered up to 75,000 tons, at not less than 50 cents a pound, c.i.f. domestic ports, purchases to be made for one year or until June 30, 1941, and this contract has since been extended to July 1, 1942.

Up to July, 1941, we were importing tin at an annual rate of 171,500 net tons, with increased shipments from the British and Dutch East Indies and the Belgian Congo.

By the close of 1940 the government stock pile contained 21,419 long tons of tin, including 89 tons produced in this country from Bolivian tin. Now that we are no longer able to count on our usual supply from the East Indies, we can still depend on Bolivia for an annual production of at least 18,000 tons to be smelted in Texas. The total visible supply of tin in Bolivia, or the probable reserve of ore there, amounts to about 520,000 tons. This can be mined at the rate of 3,200 tons a month; so that if necessary we can probably increase our imports from that country.

In other words, it is hard to conceive of a situation in which we would be thrown entirely on our own resources; and if we were, we would still have enough tin to meet our most pressing needs. There would have to be uncomfortable readjustments, but our war effort would not be seriously impeded by a lack of this important material.

Tin [a] Imported for Consumption in the United States, 1939-40, by Countries

	1939		1940	
	Long Tons	Value	Long Tons	Value
Argentina	251	$256,516	—	—
Australia	250	256,498	711	$760,641
Belgian Congo	100	123,220	4,899	5,527,493
Belgium	1,320	1,429,471	80	42,560
British Malaya	46,785	47,139,136	96,454	98,606,535
Canada	3	2,358	7	2,036
China	3,259	3,015,954	3,889	3,591,865
Hong Kong	1,062	999,133	480	415,452
Indo-China, French	25	24,877	1,241	1,340,956
Mexico	—	—	23	18,333
Netherlands	1,008	1,018,181	10	5,086
Netherlands Indies	5,316	5,442,528	12,101	12,916,449
Panama	[b]	91	[b]	98
Portugal	25	27,227	104	86,044
United Kingdom	10,698	10,855,574	4,851	4,980,862
	70,102	70,590,764	124,810	128,294,410

[a] Bars, pigs, blocks, grain, granulated, or scrap, and alloys, chief value tin, n.s.p.f.
[b] Less than 1 ton.

Salient Statistics for Tin in the United States, 1925-29 (average) and 1936-40

	1925–29 (average)	1936	1937	1938	1939	1940
Production						
From domestic mines—long tons	24	101.0	168.4	95	34	44[a]
From secondary sources "	30,600	25,000	27,100	21,000	26,000	[b]
Imports for consumption (metal) "	78,009	76,029	88,115	49,699	70,102	124,810
Exports (domestic and foreign) "	1,740	386[c]	313[c]	205[c]	2,105[c]	2,664[c]
Monthly price of Straits tin in New York:						
Highest—cents per pound	70.67	51.85	62.71	46.23	63.50	54.54
Lowest "	39.79	42.22	42.85	36.84	45.62	45.94
Average "	56.64	46.42	54.24	42.26	50.18	49.82
World Production—long tons	163,000	179,000	208,100	159,900	172,700	231,700
Ratio—United States imports to world production—percent	48	42	42	31	41	54

[a] Subject to revision.
[b] Data not available.
[c] Figures for 1936-40 cover foreign only; domestic not separatey recorded

Consumption of Primary and Secondary Tin in the United States, 1937-39, in Long Tons

	1937	1938	1939
Stocks on hand Jan. 1	71,978	25,984	25,260
Net purchases during year[a]	101,354	61,431[b]	89,018
Available supply	119,332	87,415[b]	114,278
Stocks on hand Dec. 31	25,984	25,260[b]	29,025
Total processed during year	93,348	62,155[b]	85,253
Intercompany transactions in scrap (tin content)	2,782	2,122[b]	2,390
Total consumed in manufacturing	90,566	60,033[b]	82,863
Plant losses	436	259[b]	435
Tin content of manufactured products	90,130	59,774[b]	82,428
Primary	72,928	48,116[b]	66,583[c]
Secondary	17,202	11,658[b]	15,845

[a] 1937: Primary, 82,946; secondary, 3,461; terne, 1,052; scrap, 13,895.
 1938: Primary, 50,052; secondary, 1,983; terne, 787; scrap, 8,609.
 1939: Primary, 70,732; secondary, 4,976; terne, 1,171; scrap, 12,139.
[b] Revised figures.
[c] Includes small tonnage secondary pig tin.

[2]

Steel, Heart and Life-Blood of Armaments

STEEL, the god to whom the war lords have sacrificed the comforts and pleasures of their people, must now be master of Americans until we have fashioned enough planes, carriers, battleships, tanks and guns to make victory possible.

Civilians in this country may not have to substitute guns for butter, but they will be forced to do without a great variety of objects in order to make the "arsenal of democracy" really effective.

Cutlery, and hardware of all kinds, will fast disappear from dealers' shelves, new plumbing will be but a dream, worn-out plumbing hard to repair, much less replace. Parts for all varieties of mechanical devices, from automobiles and typewriters to washing and sewing machines will be unobtainable. Even the makers of such essential products as vitamins are already finding it difficult to obtain steel for their equipment.

Only those plants producing objects directly connected with the war effort are receiving allocations: steel has only one purpose today. Five tons of it are required to make one large bomber or transport plane; many times that amount for a destroyer or submarine.

The important point is, however, that we can produce enough steel to make the thousands of planes and battleships required to win the war!

As a matter of fact, it is a very fortunate thing for the United Nations that steel does play the major role in modern warfare; for even if Hitler should have all of Europe and Japan all of Asia, we could still produce more of this precious metal than the Axis Powers.

And we are already making stupendous amounts of it. Our electrical steel production in 1941 equaled over 1,000,000 tons and may possibly go to 5,000,000 tons in 1942. And this happens to be the steel used particularly in the making of airplanes.

As for blast furnace steel we are producing ever-increasing quantities of it, too, thanks to our ability to turn out so much pig iron—a probable 83,000,000 tons in 1942, 93,000,000 tons in 1943, and possibly five more million tons the next year. (To go above 98,000,000 tons we would have to develop new mines, build new rolling mills, new blast furnaces and so forth—in other words, really start again from scratch.)

The sad part of this story is that 1942 production of pig iron cannot far exceed that for 1941 because we lack scrap iron—the same scrap iron of which we exported 25,000,000 tons during the years 1931-1941, mostly to Japan.

Pig iron may be called the "first draft" of steel. The finished product, depending upon the use for which it is destined, must contain a variety of other minerals. Some minerals make it hard, some make it tough, others make it stainless, etc.

But there is one mineral which must be present in every single kind of steel, and that is manganese, sometimes called "the starch of steel."

The consumer is not familiar with this homely mineral, so that the present potential shortage in manganese is not a matter of apparent concern to the general public. A real shortage would be a general catastrophe, however, and it is a fortunate thing for us all that our Government started a long time ago taking the measures discussed later.

Another fundamental in the making of steel is, like manganese, unappreciated by the general public. This is graphite, necessary for making foundry facings and metal castings. We use this humble carbon every day in lead-pencils, and when these begin to be scarce we will wonder why, since this country has plenty of lead, until they tell us the latter cannot be hardened any more because all the amorphous graphite we produce must be used by the iron and steel industries.

Of far more immediate interest to the man in the street are chromium and nickel, for we all realize now that the shiny trimmings on our cars and refrigerators and in our bathrooms would be impossible to replace today. Monel metal kitchen sinks, too, will not be obtainable for the duration, nor will nickel steel vacuum cleaner parts, stainless steel cutlery, and many other household articles.

The consumer's most direct contact with tungsten is as a filament in electric light bulbs. These are going to be scarce one of these days and the "substitute" kind will not be as satisfactory. But of course the most vital use of tungsten today is in steel for cutting tools. Most of us never see these tools but we are all well aware, by now, of their importance to our war effort.

Vanadium is also used in the making of steels for high-speed tools as well as those used for driving and transmission axles and gun forgings. Like tungsten and manganese, vanadium has no "eye appeal" and would be of interest only to engineers if this country were not at war. Now they mean something to us all, for we are less interested in gleaming radiator hoods than in anti-aircraft guns.

So let us take a closer look at these materials that go into the making of the "life-blood" of armaments.

Manganese

Of all the raw materials essential both to peacetime economy and national defense none is more important than manganese, "the starch of steel." Possessing none of the more spectacular qualities of nickel, aluminum and chromium, it is nevertheless more vital to our whole industrial system than any of them and "more to be desired than gold, yea than much fine gold" in time of war.

We could no more do without manganese in our machine age than we could do without coal or iron, for it is just as essential as those two minerals in the production of steel, the very "skeleton of modern industry."

Actually, manganese serves in two ways in steel manufacture. As low-grade ore, it is added to pig iron in the blast furnace. Much more important, in the form of ferromanganese it is added in all other metallurgical practice, principally in the open hearth furnace. There, by removing and controlling impurities, it helps to produce a sound, clean ingot which has suitable properties for machining, hot and cold rolling, and other processing.

Ferromanganese, which contains approximately 80 percent manganese, and 20 percent mainly iron and carbon, is normally made from high-grade (or ferro-grade) manganese ore having a minimum of about 48 percent and preferably more. A satisfactory grade of ferromanganese can be made from lower-grade ores, as was done during the last war, provided the percentages of iron and other impurities are not too high.

In the blast furnace a low-grade manganiferous ore will do—as in the case of certain other applications of manganese such as a few of its chemical uses: as a catalyst in the paint and varnish industry, to give an amethyst color to glass and china, and in the manufacture of disinfectant.

To make most steels, however, ferromanganese from the high (ferro) grade ore must be used. Not less than 35 percent of manganese will do, and sometimes the percentage must be as high as 50 percent. Curiously enough, this is not due to the fact that a great deal of manganese enters the steel—it takes usually about fourteen pounds of ferromanganese to produce one ton of steel—but the ore used in the steel must contain a high percentage of manganese for the latter to become satisfactorily alloyed.

And there's our handicap; for we who manufacture one-half of the world's steel and consume one-half of the world's total supply of manganese have plenty of the low-grade ore within our borders but little or none of the ferro-grade which is required for the making of steel.

Domestic ore is suitable, however, for use in the manufacture of dry batteries, which consume about one-third of the manganese produced in this country.

There are manganese deposits in thirty-eight states, stretching from Maine to California and from Minnesota to Texas; about fifteen hundred deposits in all. Most abundant are those in South Dakota, Montana, the Appalachian and Piedmont districts, the southern Mississippi Valley and along the Pacific coast. All of these together, however, do not now produce more than a very small percentage of our manganese needs. In 1939 they accounted for 5 percent of apparent consumption; in 1940 only 3 percent—due largely to the 27 percent increase in steel production. More manganese was mined that year but still more steel was produced, necessitating the use of increased amounts of manganese with the result that the larger domestic supply of manganese took care of a smaller percentage of our manganese needs.

The manganese producers in this country insist, however, that our output of manganese could be enormously increased if the price of the mineral were high enough. Benefication processes are being constantly studied and developed. Ferro-grade manganese ore has been produced by the Cuban-American Manganese Corporation flotation process for about ten years, and their process, besides providing a substantial nearby source of manganese for this country, also holds promise for its possible application to domestic ores.

A process by which manganese is produced in the form of manganiferous iron carbonate also offers chances of success, but it is not yet commercially available; and Anaconda Copper has worked out a successful flotation process (now in operation in a new plant at Butte, Montana) applicable to low-grade carbonate ores, which will allow this company to offer a 60 percent ore containing less than 7 percent silica, with the added advantage of greatly increasing the known reserves of carbonate ores.

In fact, Anaconda Copper engineers are so sure of the efficiency of their new process that the company is building a plant at Butte with an annual capacity of 100,000 tons a year of ferro-grade ore and has arranged to sell 80,000 tons of 58 percent ore a year to the Metal Reserves Corporation over the next three years.

The Bureau of Mines is, naturally, also working on the problem of domestic production and they have announced the development of a method for making electrolytic manganese. This process, however, is still in the pilot plant stage and its real success will depend on price and its adaptability to our domestic ores. Moreover, it is not certain that the metal thus obtained would be economically applicable to the needs of the steel industry.

Consequently, most experts agree that unless this or some other process can be made to work we cannot depend on our domestic manganese deposits for the bulk of our requirements. The consensus of opinion seems to be summed up in the following table from the Tariff Commission, made before the outbreak of the present war, giving a comparison between domestic and foreign ores:

MANGANESE ORE

DOMESTIC	IMPORTED
1. Mostly low grade.	1. Medium to high grade.
2. Very variable in grade.	2. Fairly uniform in grade.
3. Generally contain undesirable impurities (silica and phosphorus).	3. Generally free from undesirable impurities.
4. Production and shipments irregular and usually in small lots.	4. Supply uniform and dependable and in large lots.

Due to the stimulus of the war, manganese mining in the United States improved somewhat in 1941, but even so was able to supply only 3 percent of our apparent domestic consumption—due, once more, to the increase in steel production. Mine shipments amounted to 40,123 long tons of ore (35 percent or more manganese), far less than in 1918, when they totaled 305,869 long tons.

The high-grade ores we need have been coming from Russia, which for the past five years has supplied 31 percent of our consumption of manganese; from the Gold Coast, which is responsible for 27 percent, Cuba 13 percent, India 12 percent and Brazil 11 percent.

Since the war, shipments from Russia have been cut off and shipping rates from the other sources have been tremendously increased—some as much as 500 percent. Altogether, we imported 1,294,316 tons of ferro-grade manganese in 1940.

Brazil, which produced 228,000 tons in 1937, contains plentiful deposits, but transportation facilities in that country are so meager we will have to help build railroads before we can depend on supplies of Brazilian ore. The largest developed deposits are in the State of Minas Geraes; smaller ones now being exploited are in Bahia, while very extensive beds are reported in Matto Grosso and Pará. According to Brazilian figures, the known deposits in Minas Geraes contain reserves of about 12,000,000 tons of high-grade (40-55 percent) ore; and ore mined in that district was recently purchased by an American company (Morra da Mina) for $4,000,000. It is noted in the Brazilian Year Book that the Japanese have shown marked interest in the manganese deposits.

While the deposits in Cuba are both smaller and lower-grade than those in Brazil, Cuba offers the surest possibilities as a source of supply for the United States until Brazil is better equipped with transportation facilities. The Cuban-American Manganese Corporation, which began operations in 1932 and is actively engaged in exploiting manganese deposits in Oriente Province, has developed a successful benefication process and is producing at the rate of 130,000 tons of high-grade ore a year.

Let us consider now just what our situation is in the present emergency. One expert, Emeny, has estimated our manganese requirements for two years as follows:

		First Year	*Second Year*
1.	Ferro-grade (metallurgical uses)	790,000	1,580,000
2.	Ferro-grade (chemical uses)	35,000	70,000
3.	Ferruginous (spiegeleisen)	511,000	1,022,000
4.	Manganiferous iron ore	2,500,000	5,000,000

Our domestic ore reserves would be ample for the last three items, so that the real procurement problem revolves around the first alone; but this is problem enough, since we have no assurance that our domestic production of high-grade manganese could amount to more than 279,000 long tons in two years—and then only at a very high price.

If we add to this the amount of manganese now being regularly imported from Brazil and Cuba we are still about a million tons short of our emergency requirements. And in neither of the latter countries could a manganese industry be greatly expanded overnight. For non-strategic uses chilled white iron could be employed in place of steel made with ferromanganese, and in some steel sheets a less perfect finish could do, but in all the important uses of steel no substitute exists for that made with high-grade manganese.

The only solution, therefore, open to our Government at the beginning of the war was the accumulation of stock piles large enough to take care of a two-year emergency and to start now to build up as active a manganese industry as possible in this country as well as in both Brazil and Cuba.

The strategic aspects of this essential mineral were made the constant preoccupation of R. C. Allen, Consultant, Ferrous Minerals and Alloys, in the Office of Production Management, and further advice has been sought from the Technologic Committee on Manganese of the National Academy of Sciences and the National Research Council. The latter was formed to review projects for developing new processes for the recovery of manganese from low-grade domestic ores and to study the conservation of our manganese resources; and the former, composed of nine eminent scientists and engineers from government and industry, has been studying ways and means of reducing our manganese requirements during an emergency.

As to the situation on Government stock piles of manganese, two agencies of the United States Government—the Metals Reserve Company and the Procurement Division of the Treasury Department—have signed and are signing numerous contracts with both domestic producers and importers for the delivery of ferromanganese ore for Government stock piles over a period of years.

Imports up to July, 1941, were at the annual rate of 1,150,000 net tons—as compared with 1,294,361 in 1940. Russia and Gold Coast im-

Salient Statistics of the Manganese Industry in the United States, 1925-29 (Average) and 1936-40, in Long Tons

	1925-29 (average)	1936	1937	1938	1939	1940
Manganese ore:						
Total shipments containing 35 percent or more Mn	59,312	32,119	40,241	25,321	29,307	40,123
Shipments of metallurgical ore	41,892[a]	18,557	26,419	16,989	18,580	27,158
Shipments of battery ore	17,420	7,747	6,447	4,959	7,767	9,271
Imports for consumption	600,000	813,362	911,919	483,586	627,131	1,282,079
Stocks in bonded warehouses at end of year	304,000	366,381	681,290	842,048	903,561	913,016
Indicated consumption [ad] (55 percent or more Mn)	659,000	848,491	954,503	509,930	656,438	1,322,202
Ferro-alloys:						
Production of ferromanganese	306,360	316,000	376,443	242,994	270,111	459,538
Imports of ferromanganese [bcd]	50,590	30,593	23,888	21,118	33,414	8,573
Production of spiegeleisen	95,463	95,137	[e]	11,311	91,491	101,892
Imports of spiegeleisen [b]	7,298	52,011	16,841	17,248	38,264	15,585
Exports of spiegeleisen and ferromanganese	3,769	466	1,725	247	2,923	13,036
Stocks of ferromanganese in bonded warehouses	7,765[cd]	9,902	11,788	8,392	4,253	1,514

[a] Includes small quantity of miscellaneous ore.
[b] Imports for consumption.
[c] Manganese content.
[d] Includes small quantity of other manganese alloys.
[e] Bureau of Mines not at liberty to publish figures.

ports had declined considerably, but those from India, Cuba and South Africa had increased, as well as those from Brazil, and a new source of supply had been opened up in the Philippines—which now is of no practical value to us.

Stocks in warehouses on June 1, 1941, amounted to slightly above 1,000,000 tons, including the supply in Government stock piles of 200,000 tons.

This amount will not last very long, with our new production program really under way, so that the manganese deposits of this country are going to come in for some very extensive development, and effective benefication processes will become more and more valuable. The long-debated question as to the value of the mines of this country is certainly going to be settled this time.

Contracts and Deliveries of Manganese Ore to the United States Government, 1940, by States and Countries of Origin, in Long Tons

	METALS RESERVE CO.		TREASURY DEPARTMENT		Total
Origin	Contracted	Deliveries	Contracted	Deliveries	Deliveries
United States:					
California	80,000	—	—	—	—
Colorado	20,000	—	—	—	—
Montana	400,000	—	—	—	—
Nevada	150,000	—	7,500	—	—
New Mexico	240,000	—	—	—	—
Pennsylvania	180,000	—	—	—	—
Tennessee	15,000	—	—	—	—
Virginia	100,000	—	—	—	—
West Virginia	150,000	—	—	—	—
Total Domestic	1,335,000	—	7,500	—	—
Other countries:					
Brazil	18,000	—	—	—	—
Chile	2,000	2,000	—	—	2,000
Cuba	248,000	—	2,500	—	—
India, British	283,700	14,700	7,918	7,952	22,652
Mexico	10,000	—	—	—	—
Philippine Islands	53,000	3,500	31,500	27,155	30,655
Union of South Africa	199,500	8,600	13,882	14,046	22,646
U.S.S.R.	1,000	1,000	—	—	1,000
Total foreign	815,200	29,800	55,800	49,153	78,953
Total	2,150,200	29,800	63,300	49,153	78,953

Manganese and Manganiferous Ores Shipped by Mines in the United States in 1940, by States

	ORE CONTAINING 35 PERCENT OR MORE MN		
	Shippers	Long Tons	Value
Metallurgical:			
Alabama	1	57	a
Arizona	3	311	$4,027
Arkansas	2	6,079	a
California	2	158	a
Colorado	1	224	a
Georgia	5	3,572	68,508
Idaho	—	—	—
Massachusetts	—	—	—
Michigan	—	—	—
Minnesota	—	—	—
Montana	1[b]	8,230	a
Nevada	1	210	a
New Mexico	1	45	a
North Carolina	—	—	—
Tennessee	6[b]	6,983	105,022
Utah	1	27	a
Virginia	9[b]	1,043	16,583
West Virginia	1	219	a
Undistributed	—	—	423,532
Total metallurgical	34	27,158	617,672
Battery: Montana	2[c]	9,271	458,966
Miscellaneous:			
Alabama	2	186	
Arizona	1	58	51,969
Montana	2[b]	1,842	
Tennessee	10[b]	435	15,714
Virginia	9[b]	1,173	24,703
Total Miscellaneous	24	3,694	92,386
	51	40,123	1,169,024

[a] Included under "Undistributed."

[b] One producer in Montana, three in Tennessee, and five in Virginia shipped both metallurgical and miscellaneous ore.

[c] Mills through which all ore was shipped; producers not counted.

Manganese and Manganiferous Ores Shipped by Mines in the United States in 1940, by States (*continued*)

	ORE CONTAINING 10 TO 35 PERCENT MN			ORE CONTAINING 5 TO 10 PERCENT MN	
Shippers	*Long Tons*	*Value*	*Shippers*	*Long Tons*	*Value*
2	342	a	—	—	—
—	—	—	—	—	—
1	1,075	a	—	—	—
1	87	a	—	—	—
1	3,303	a	—	—	—
10	10,088	$63,218	1	205	a
1	313	a	—	—	—
1	1,900	a	—	—	—
—	—	—	1	18,617 }	$2,002,673
3	248,732	935,679	4	797,642 }	
1	3,617	a	—	—	—
1	4,613	a	—	—	—
2	36,835	a	—	—	—
1	190	a	—	—	—
2	2,327	a	—	—	—
7	2,102	13,134	—	—	—
5	4,482	29,903	2	77	a
—	—	—	—	—	—
—	—	302,726	—	—	709
39	320,006	1,344,660	8	816,541	2,003,382
—	—	—	—	—	—
—	—	—	—	—	—
—	—	—	—	—	—
—	—	—	—	—	—
—	—	—	—	—	—
39	320,006	1,344,660	8	816,541	2,003,382

Manganese Ore (35 percent or more Mn) Imported
for Consumption in the United States,
1938-40, by Countries

COUNTRY	MANGANESE ORE (LONG TONS)			MN CONTENT (LONG TONS)		
	1938	1939	1940	1938	1939	1940
Brazil	29,698	42,713	168,241	13,307	19,499	75,060
Chile	—	49	7,849	—	23	3,718
Cuba	131,422	105,936	130,646	61,534	51,718	64,175
Gold Coast	126,857	242,923	246,983	63,890	122,769	124,221
India, British	25,480	89,545	189,473	13,121	45,556	95,100
Netherlands Indies	—	—	5,245	—	—	2,753
Philippine Islands	4,002	6,966	43,515	1,600	3,483	21,824
Union of South Africa	—	3,401	177,739	—	1,697	78,508
U.S.S.R.	166,042	135,243	311,748	80,673	68,881	151,367
Other countries	85	353	640	43	184	375
	483,586	627,129	1,282,079	234,168	313,810	617,101

COUNTRY	VALUE		
	1938	1939	1940
Brazil	$220,328	$366,597	$1,678,395
Chile	—	300	155,680
Cuba	2,242,425	1,689,547	3,059,735
Gold Coast	1,500,813	3,019,368	4,468,383
India, British	236,945	1,054,718	2,323,880
Netherlands Indies	—	—	144,131
Philippine Islands	44,075	89,784	627,243
Union of South Africa	—	45,716	1,802,537
U.S.S.R.	2,661,557	2,204,304	3,947,706
Other countries	13,254	27,716	24,137
	6,919,397	8,498,050	18,231,887

MANGANESE ORE

IMPORTED INTO THE UNITED STATES 1940

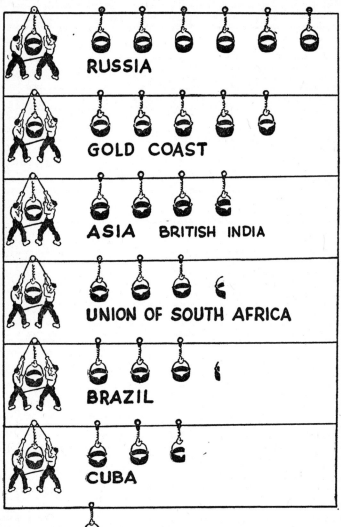

RUSSIA

GOLD COAST

ASIA   BRITISH INDIA

UNION OF SOUTH AFRICA

BRAZIL

CUBA

EACH ⚫ REPRESENTS 50,000 LONG TONS

MANGANESE ORE -

WORLD PRODUCTION - 1937

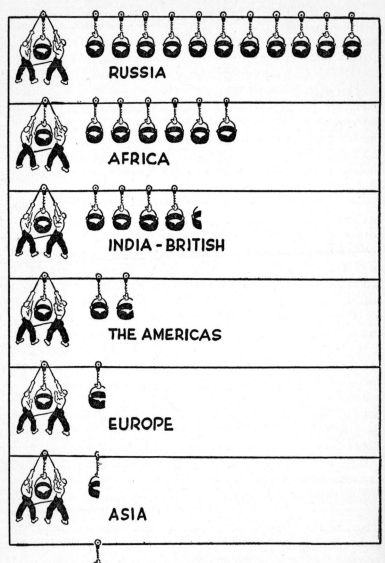

RUSSIA

AFRICA

INDIA - BRITISH

THE AMERICAS

EUROPE

ASIA

EACH REPRESENTS 250,000 METRIC TONS

Graphite

Taken from the Greek word meaning "to write," the term *graphite* immediately suggests the lead-pencil, which is the most familiar—though not by any means the most extensive—application of plumbago, or black lead. Its use in crucibles for making steel and other alloys, while far more important, is perhaps not as well known.

Chemically, this mineral is pure carbon, just as charcoal and diamonds are, but the physical characteristics of graphite are markedly different from those of the other two. For instance, graphite is one of the softest minerals while diamond is the hardest.

There are three commercial types of graphite: amorphous, crystalline lump and crystalline flake. As a matter of fact, all are crystalline in structure, but in amorphous graphite, the most abundant type, the crystals are so small as to be invisible to the naked eye and the substance has a dull, lusterless appearance, while in both the lump and flake varieties the individual crystals are in evidence.

With the possible exception of Russia, the largest producing area is in Central Europe (Bavaria, Moravia and Austria) but the graphite found there is mostly low-grade and does not figure largely in international trade. Chosen, off the coast of China, has become in recent years a large exporter of amorphous graphite and a not insignificant source of flake graphite. But the principal exporter of flake graphite to the United States is Madagascar; while Ceylon is the chief source of crystalline and amorphous imported into this country, and we import amorphous also from Mexico.

There are deposits of graphite in the United States: in New York State on the St. Lawrence River (amorphous), in Montana (crystalline), in Alabama (flake), and in Michigan, Nevada and Rhode Island (amorphous); but we import nearly all the natural graphite we use.

Flake from Madagascar and crystalline from Ceylon are essential in a strategic sense, since they are indispensable in the manufacture of crucibles used for melting other metals, especially the bronze and other copper alloys needed in the building of all kinds of ships. Some of these crucibles weigh as much as 350 pounds, with an estimated capacity of 2,500 pounds of bronze, and all are made of one-half graphite, the rest being clay and sand.

During the last war makers of such crucibles would use nothing but Ceylon plumbago; now they are just as insistent on Madagascar flake, though a few of them add Ceylon graphite for certain products, and one uses a small quantity of Alabama flake for a special type of crucible.

About five thousand tons of flake graphite are used every year for this purpose in normal times; while smaller amounts of both flake and crystalline go into retorts, stopper heads and nozzles, as well as into lubricants, all of them accounting for only 10 percent of the total consumption.

Amorphous graphite, from Ceylon and Mexico and from domestic mines, is also used in lubricants (about 10 percent of the total used); lead-pencils (also 10 percent); twice as much in the manufacture of paints, to which it gives a remarkable resistance to acid fumes, heat and corrosion; electric brushes; carbons for dry batteries; special furnace blocks; electrodes; rubber compounds and molds, and stove polish. Its most important application, however, is in the iron and steel industries for making foundry facings and metal castings.

Molds for casting molten metal are made by carefully burying a pattern in sand which has been treated to keep its shape after the pattern has been removed. The surface of this mold is then "greased" (like a cake pan) with graphite, which gives it a smooth surface and keeps the molten metal from sticking.

Only natural amorphous graphite can be used for these molds, but fortunately artificial graphite is possible for some of its other applications. Due to the high quality of the synthetic product that can be obtained it is becoming increasingly popular. It is made in electric furnaces from anthracite or petroleum coke. In the United States the largest producer of synthetic graphite is the Acheson Graphite Company, the founder of which, Dr. Edward Acheson, invented the first successful process for making artificial graphite.

Moreover, carbon more or less graphitized is a by-product of several electro-chemical processes, and under certain circumstances this material may replace natural amorphous graphite. In other words, natural graphite is no longer absolutely necessary for all its uses in amorphous form, although for most applications related to defense production it cannot be replaced.

There are no known substitutes for the crystalline graphite used in crucibles, and these are still essential for the melting of non-ferrous metals, but there is a noticeable increase in the use of electric furnaces for the melting of steel.

Since 1936 we have been producing about 5,000 short tons a year of natural graphite and importing about 22,000 tons, chiefly amorphous. From Canada we normally import about 1,000 tons a year of artificial graphite, 300 tons of natural flake and more than that amount of amorphous.

From September, 1939, to August, 1940, our imports of graphite showed a large increase over the preceding twelve-month period: imports of amorphous rose from 34 to 41.6 million pounds; those of crystalline (lump, chip and dust) from 0.5 to 2 million pounds; and those of flake from 4.2 to 6 million pounds.

Even before the fall of France procurement of Madagascar flake was becoming difficult; after the armistice signed at Compiègne none could be obtained for some time. As Madagascar had recognized the Vichy Government the British blockaded its ports, and it was only after major diplomatic maneuvers that we were able to procure Madagascar graphite, including a small purchase for the Government stock pile. These imports amounted to about three times the average quantities imported annually during the last five years, but estimated requirements had meantime been increased to nearly 400 tons a month, or more than twice our normal needs.

Should our supply from both Madagascar and Ceylon be completely shut off, we could still import from Mexico, which shipped us 9,070 short tons in 1939, 60 percent more in 1940, and could probably increase its output at a higher price for graphite; but Mexican graphite, being all of the amorphous type, would not replace the special varieties we need from Ceylon and Madagascar. Careful use of what we now have and the building up of a stock pile as fast as possible seems to be the only answer to this particular procurement problem.

Graphite Imported for Consumption in the United States, 1936-40, by Kinds

| | AMORPHOUS | | | | CRYSTALLINE | | | | |
| | NATURAL | | ARTIFICIAL | | LUMP AND CHIP | | DUST | | FLAKE | |
YEAR	Short Tons	Value	Short Tons	Value	Short Tons	Value	Short Tons	Value	Short Tons	Value
1936	20,160	$344,499	1,635	$63,804	251	$18,107	68	$4,090	2,057	$136,162
1937	25,354	512,162	802	31,562	482	41,499	321	17,600	2,634	149,492
1938	14,676	247,789	500	19,870	41	3,074	168	10,643	1,620	90,663
1939	18,675	269,046	413	15,383	a	a	602a	30,421a	2,260	110,476
1940	23,766	487,675	260	9,187	a	a	752a	54,027a	6,551	340,396

[a] Lump and chip included with dust.

World Production of Natural Graphite, 1915-34 (5-year Averages), 1935-37 (3-year Average), 1938, and 1939, in Metric Tons

(Compiled by L. P. Lounsbery)

COUNTRY	1915-19 (AVERAGE)	1920-24 (AVERAGE)	1925-29 (AVERAGE)
Argentina	—	—	—
Australia:			
New South Wales	100	18	12
Queensland	—	—	—
South Australia	—	—	—
Brazil[c]	13	10	4
Bulgaria	—	—	—
Canada	2,481	1,172	1,756
Ceylon[c]	21,042	9,088	13,618
Chosen[c]	7,679	15,034	18,484
Czechoslovakia	26,841[e]	13,751	29,276
France	886	415	734
Germany:			
Austria	19,657[f]	11,557	19,083
Bavaria	31,308	21,696	17,548
Greenland	—	753	—
India, British	349	29	8
Indo-China[c]	6,160	—	289[g]
Italy	9,151	5,722	8,487
Japan	1,380	778	578
Madagascar[c]	16,776	9,929	14,141
Mexico	3,059	4,340	5,699
Morocco:			
French[c]	a	—	21
Spanish	—	—	—
Norway	—	2	—
Spain	1,184	1,923	580
Sweden	101	1	—
Union of South Africa	64	50	51
U.S.S.R.	a	a	3,992
United States:			
Amorphous	3,999	3,059	2,840
Crystalline	4,494	1,672	2,133
Total[k]	156,724	100,999	139,334

[a] Data not available.

[b] Less than 1 ton.

[c] Exports.

[d] Quantity not available; value reported as follows: 1935, $79,781; 1936, $88,812; 1937, $125,343; 1938, $41,590; 1939, data not available.

[e] Average based upon production of Bohemia and Moravia, which before 1918 formed part of Austria.

World Production of Natural Graphite, 1915-34 (5-year Averages), 1935-37 (3-year Average), 1938, and 1939, in Metric Tons (*continued*)

(Compiled by L. P. Lounsbery)

1930-34 (AVERAGE)	1935-37 (AVERAGE)	1938	1939
—	14	28	—
18	10	—	a
—	16	10	a
15	b	—	—
4	4	a	a
—	—	—	23
790	d	d	d
8,677	15,174	11,972	22,756
23,721	42,937	50,348	78,501
4,187	3,313	a	a
46	—	a	a
14,653	19,786	16,852	a
21,333	23,166	28,106	a
—	20	a	a
71	509	465	951
—	3	a	a
3,997	5,255	5,485	a
572	1,389h	a	a
6,111	9,668	13,433	a
3,521	9,480	9,611	9,815
108	324	406	a
—	—	73	a
1,206	2,485	3,802	a
—	—	—	a
—	52	48	165
53	63	54	59
32,333i	a	a	a
j	j	j	j
j	j	j	j
121,416	133,668	140,694	112,270

f Average based upon production of Lower Austria and Styria only. Data covering production of Bohemia and Moravia shown under Czechoslovakia.

g Concentrates.

h Average for 1935-36; data for 1937 not available.

i Average for 1932-34; data for 1930-31 not available.

j Bureau of Mines not at liberty to publish figures.

k Sum of figures given in table only; probably incomplete.

NATURAL GRAPHITE

WORLD PRODUCTION 1938

EACH ♦ REPRESENTS 5,000 METRIC TONS

Chromium

Chromium is one of the rare metals—that is to say, it is among the large "oxygen" group which makes up that tiny 5 percent of the earth's crust not composed of the few abundant elements such as iron, sodium, silicon and calcium.

More than that, chromium is one of the few metals seldom seen in its pure state; it is, in fact, not available except as a plating on other metals. The "chromium" of commerce is really chromite, the principal ore of chromium, which is a mineral containing the oxides of chromium and iron plus alumina and magnesia; and its value is determined by the ratio between iron and chromium in the ore.

Chromite happens to be not only one of the most refractory of ores but also the least impressive in appearance, so that chromium might never have been discovered or used but for its occurrence in another mineral. This one, exceedingly beautiful, was first noticed in 1765 by a Russian geologist near Ekaterinburg. The brilliant red, four-sided prisms he found, later named "crocoite," were collected by amateurs and used by artists for a pigment. They were also studied by various chemists, but their valuable content was not discovered until the Frenchman, Vauquelin, finally isolated the glistening silvery metal in the form of chromium carbide, in 1797.

The very next year chromite ore was found in the Ural Mountains, which remained the only source of that mineral for about thirty years. During that time the users of chromium, mostly paint manufacturers, had to depend on supplies that were first loaded on rafts, floated to navigable waters leading to the Obi River, and thence transported to the Arctic Sea for transshipment to the ports of Western Europe— which they usually reached three years after they left the mines.

It was, therefore, a godsend to American makers of chromium paints when, about a century ago, Isaac Tyson of Baltimore discovered a deposit on his property in Hartford County, Maryland. An English gardener was the *deus ex machina*. Having worked in his youth in a paint factory in Scotland this man recognized the black stones which, when ground, yielded the valuable chromium compound.

The paint industry is still a large consumer of chromium; we tan much of our leather by means of chrome salts; but the metal's greatest value right now lies in its ability to form an alloy with steel.

Chromite mixed with a carbonaceous material in an electric furnace yields ferrochromium, the basic alloy of the metal, containing between 66 and 72 percent chromium, varying percentages of carbon, not more than 0.5 percent of manganese, from 1 percent upward of silicon, and the remaining percentage in iron and some impurities such as sulfur and phosphorus.

To make chromium steel this alloy is added to the steel bath, where it gives up varying percentages of its chromium according to the process employed. A moderate proportion of this metal tends to make the steel corrosion-resistant, hard, tough and strong. The highest percentage of chromium in any steel (certain stainless and others) is approximately 28, while only 1 percent or less is needed for some construction materials.

Steels are by no means the only products containing chromium. The list below shows the more familiar ways in which chromium compounds are used:

Ceramics	Pigments
Electroplating	Paints & Varnishes
Electrocells	Refractories
Glazes	Tanning
Inks	Textile Dyeing

Strictly military uses of this metal for which there are no adequate substitutes include basic chromium sulfate, practically indispensable in the tanning of certain types of leather; sodium bichromate, essential in the dye for "olive drab"; and, above all, the many special steels which have direct military value—such as those for armor plate, armor-piercing projectiles, high-speed cutting tools, machinery parts and most forms of transport equipment.

In fact, the steel industry consumes more than three-fourths of the supply of chromite, either as an alloying element or in refractories. Since the latter account for more than half of that 75 percent the possible use of substitutes for that purpose offers some hope of a substantial saving during the present emergency.

In the case of a much less vital application of the metal—as an electrical resistance material, for which a chrome-nickel alloy is used—it is also possible to replace the chromium.

The United States was at one time the leading producer of chromite, as we are still today the world's largest consumer, using an average of about 300,000 long tons a year. Most of this we now import from Rhodesia, which has the most extensive, high-grade chromite beds in the world.

The next largest high-grade deposits are in Turkey and Russia; Canada, Cuba, Brazil, Greece, India, New Caledonia, Yugoslavia and the Union of South Africa also produce considerable amounts of chromite.

In the United States there are over a thousand known deposits, but unfortunately most of them not only are small and low in grade but also located on the West Coast, far from consumption centers. Consequently, in most cases they cannot be operated profitably except at a price about three times the prevailing one.

Under stress of the war 3,614 long tons of chromite were produced in 1939; only 2,662 long tons in 1940. Nearly all of this (in the form of concentrates containing about 43 percent Cr_2O_3) came from the Pilliken mine in California, where operations were conducted by the Rustless Mining Company. Very much smaller shipments came from Fresno, Del Norte, Placer, Plumas, Siskiyou and Shasta Counties, California, and from Grant County, Oregon.

Meanwhile the Bureau of Mines has been carrying on extensive operations to discover and appraise all chromium deposits in the country, and large-scale experiments have been conducted at the most promising beds in Stillwater County, Montana. The Bureau of Mines has also been investigating all possible means of economically recovering chromite from the low-grade ores found in this country.

If a process now being developed in Canada for manufacturing ferrochromium from low-grade ores should ever prove commercially successful, our deposits would gain immeasurably in value. Their usefulness may also be considerably enhanced by another method, now being tested in this country, by which the electric furnace may be used to smelt low-grade ores. Until these processes are proved we must continue to import from Rhodesia and other British and French possessions (India, New Caledonia and South Africa) which, with Cuba, furnish us with the chromium we use today.

As long as Britannia and the United States rule the waves these imports are assured us. Should it become impossible to receive them, we would have to fall back on our own resources, however expensive it might be to exploit them. At a price we could probably produce

100,000 tons a year, or possibly more. At this rate, with stocks on hand—estimated at 140,000 tons—we would have resources of at least 300,000 tons for two years. This figure, which would not include any chromium procured by secondary recovery or possible shipments from Alaska or Canada, would bring us within 40,000 tons of what, in 1940, were our estimated war requirements for two years. Now, it is believed that 900,000 tons will be needed in one year.

While these estimated requirements do not include non-essential uses, the 1940 figures still represent an amount over twice the total average chromite consumption of Great Britain, France, Germany, Italy and Japan during 1925-29. It is, therefore, quite possible that for

World Production of Crude Chromite, 1936-40, by Countries, in Metric Tons [a] (Compiled by L. P. Lounsbery)

	1936	1937	1938	1939	1940
Australia (New South Wales)	422	466	967	[b]	[b]
Brazil (exports)	3,890	2,980	934	3,554	4,572
Bulgaria	270	2,350	1,745	4,251	[b]
Canada (shipments)	837	3,876	—	—	[b]
Cuba [c]	71,086	94,592	40,163	67,061	52,789
Cyprus (shipments)	508	1,641	5,667	[b]	[b]
Greece	47,347	52,620	42,464	57,091	[b]
Guatemala [c]	—	—	—	1,933	—
India, British	50,280	63,307	44,858	49,925	[b]
Japan	39,039	[d]	[d]	[d]	[b]
Levant	—	—	500	[b]	[b]
New Caledonia	47,840	48,022	52,216	52,000	55,790
Norway	—	176	508	[b]	[b]
Philippine Islands (exports)	11,891	69,856	66,911	126,749	[b]
Sierra Leone	—	741	505	10,755	[b]
Southern Rhodesia	183,395	275,617	186,019	139,083	[b]
Turkey (Asia Minor)	163,880	192,508	213,630	191,644	[b]
Union of South Africa	175,669	168,620	176,561	160,014	163,646
U.S.S.R.	217,000	[d]	[d]	[d]	[b]
United Kingdom	—	305	473	[b]	[b]
United States (shipments)	273	2,358	825	3,672	2,705
Yugoslavia	54,044	59,932	58,470	59,527	[b]
	1,068,000	1,280,000	1,133,000	1,167,000	[b]

[a] In addition to countries listed, chromite mining was reported in Albania in 1938; no production figures are available.
[b] Data not yet available.
[c] Imports into the United States.
[d] Estimate included in total.

the emergency our civilian population could submit to far more drastic reductions in the use of chromium and release still further supplies for military needs.

Second on the list of essential materials named in the Strategic Materials Act of June 7, 1939, chromium has been a special preoccupation of the officials entrusted with the accumulation of stock piles. They first placed large orders in Turkey, some of which have already been delivered; then they started intensive development of chromite mines in Alaska by placing an order for twenty-five long tons with a mine at Seldorea. This was later canceled because of non-delivery, but the deliveries from Turkey in 1940 amounted to 27,460 gross tons.

Total contracts awarded by the Procurement Division of the Treasury Department in 1940 for the purchase of chrome ore totaled 97,200 gross tons. And deliveries that year totaled 57,254 gross tons, of which 29,794 came from Rhodesia; the remainder from Turkey.

The Metals Reserve Company also awarded large contracts for chromite—100,000 tons of refractory grade chromite from the Philippines and 100,000 tons of chemical grade from the Union of South Africa, but it is not definitely known how much of the Philippines chromite was delivered before the Japanese attack.

Crude Chromite Imported into the United States, 1936-40, by Countries

COUNTRY	1936 (LONG TONS)	1937 (LONG TONS)	1938 (LONG TONS)	1939 (LONG TONS)	1940 LONG TONS		
					Gross Weight	Chromic Oxide Content	VALUE
Africa[a]	120,011	277,420	168,299	118,233	285,559	136,831	$3,969,559
Cuba	69,963	93,098	39,529	66,002	51,955	16,995	345,180
Greece	26,688	24,583	10,000	11,000	14,041	6,174	174,687
India, British	14,795	23,939	4,051	16,468	32,644	16,671	548,045
New Caledonia	65,450	51,831	28,520	14,359	42,861	22,594	599,020
Philippine Is.	4,986	43,648	78,233	71,914	156,566	66,849	1,265,400
Turkey	19,490	39,391	20,392	16,632	70,081	33,638	1,799,861
U.S.S.R.	2,310	—	—	—	—	—	—
Other countries	565	6	3,061	2,903	3,982	1,920	53,018
	324,258	553,916	352,085	317,511	657,689	301,672	8,754,770

[a] Originated in Southern Rhodesia and Union of South Africa; recorded by Foreign and Domestic Commerce as imported from Union of South Africa, Other British South Africa, Other British West Africa, and Mozambique.

Chromium was placed on full priority control in July 1941 and the OPM (now WPB) announced that even our estimated 1941 consumption of about 900,000 net tons of chromite would have to be met largely by imports.

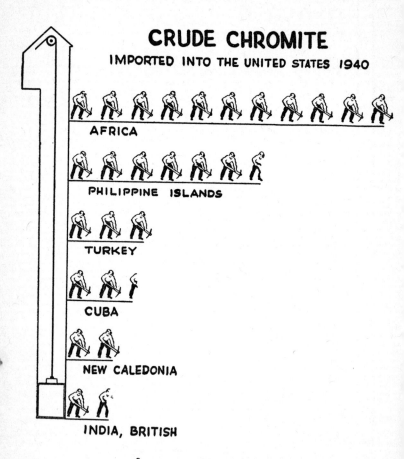

CRUDE CHROMITE
IMPORTED INTO THE UNITED STATES 1940

AFRICA

PHILIPPINE ISLANDS

TURKEY

CUBA

NEW CALEDONIA

INDIA, BRITISH

EACH [figure] REPRESENTS 25,000 LONG TONS

CRUDE CHROMITE

WORLD PRODUCTION 1940

RUSSIA - ESTIMATED -

TURKEY

PHILIPPINE ISLANDS - ESTIMATED -

UNION OF SOUTH AFRICA

SOUTHERN RHODESIA

CUBA

YUGOSLAVIA

NEW CALEDONIA

EACH REPRESENTS 25,000 METRIC TONS

Nickel

Nickel has one of the longest records in mineral history. The Persians of Darius' day believed that the "heaven-sent" blades of their mythological heroes were fashioned from this element in meteoric iron, and it was used by the ancient Chinese in their alloy, paktong.

In the Occident, however, nickel was not discovered until about the middle of the eighteenth century when copper and silver miners in Saxony were vexed by an unknown substance which kept cropping up in what looked like promising ores. These superstitious Germans, believing "Old Nick" had bewitched their mines, named the shiny metal after him.

Gradually the nature and uses of this new-found element were discovered and small deposits were found in America and several countries of Europe. Then, about 1886, the enormous nickel mines of Sudbury, Ontario, Canada, were opened up—largely through the efforts of a small group of American business men—and for a while production outstripped demand.

That condition was soon corrected, however, by the development, in France, of alloy steels for armor plate and munitions; and since then a multitude of uses for nickel and nickel steels have been developed, until today nickel is an essential raw material in every industrial country.

Years ago large deposits were discovered in New Caledonia, but the Sudbury mines produce over 85 percent of the world's supply of nickel. Moreover, the Sudbury ores are of the sulfide type, which is the most important of the nickel ores. Those in New Caledonia are of the silicate variety; while the commercially unimportant arsenical ores are found in northern Ontario and to some extent in Saxony.

Still another source of nickel has recently been developed—recovery as a by-product from electrolytic copper refineries. In 1938 we produced 377 metric tons by this method as well as 2,300 tons by secondary recovery from scrap (old automobiles and armor plate of naval vessels).

Figures for 1939 are incomplete, but those for Canada which are available (102,559 metric tons) and New Caledonia (9,300) show an important increase. The same is true of our consumption for that year (23,400 tons in 1938) though complete statistics are not available.

World consumption, which was estimated at 204,000,000 pounds in 1938, had risen to 256,000,000 pounds in 1939 and has risen substantially since.

The reason, of course, for the increased consumption of nickel in the last years has been its need for the production of steel, to which it gives hardness, toughness and strength. However, the effects produced by different amounts of nickel are amazingly divergent.

If more than 10 percent nickel is added, the steel gets softer instead of harder when it is heated and chilled; between 24 and 32 percent nickel gives a high electrical resistance; while 36 percent nickel alloy neither expands nor contracts, making it especially useful for measuring-tapes. Only 2 percent more and an alloy wire will expand and contract at the same rate as glass—ideal for the wires that lead in through the glass of an electric light bulb; a little more than double the percentage of nickel (to 78) and you have the alloy with an exceedingly high magnetic permeability which has revolutionized the manufacture of undersea cables.

Armor plate is not the only strictly military use. Armor-piercing projectiles, gun barrels, recoil cylinders and other things all require a certain amount of nickel. There is not a great deal of this mineral in any one of them, but the qualities it imparts are of such vital significance that the metal has an importance completely out of proportion to the quantity required.

Moreover, these strictly military applications of nickel are very far from being the only ones of importance during a national emergency. Modern automotive and aircraft construction are dependent on the nickel steels; and this is true also of railroad, power and oil-well equipment, architectural and bridge constructions, mining and excavating, shop and farm machinery, and the machine tools of which we are already experiencing a shortage.

These are but the outstanding products for which nickel is essential. We have not even mentioned the many uses of monel metal in all types of building, nor the application of nickel in electro-plating; much less its many uses in the chemical industry.

Obviously, then, we could not do without nickel under normal circumstances, much less during a war emergency. In 1940 we imported 140,497,158 pounds of metallic nickel and alloys from Canada, 5,000 pounds of ore and metal from the Philippines and 567,639 pounds of metallic nickel and alloys from Europe (454,551 pounds from the United Kingdom, 107,660 pounds from Norway).

It is extremely fortunate for us that our principal source of supply lies right next door and in a country consistently friendly to us. Furthermore, the Canadian nickel industry is largely under the control of one company, International Nickel. They are making every effort to provide us with an adequate supply of nickel, and they have installed additional facilities for the refining not only of the increased output of their own mines but also of the accumulated matte stock and the current matte production of Falconbridge Nickel Mines, Ltd., part of which used to be refined in Norway.

Salient Statistics for Nickel, 1938-40

		1938	1939	1940
United States:				
Production (all by-products of copper refining) short tons		416	394	554
Secondary production	"	2,300	2,920	a
Imports[b]	"	29,546	64,796	92,468
Exports[c]	"	6,581	10,167	11,994
Price per pound[d]	cents	35	35	35
Canada:				
Production	short tons	105,286	113,053	a
Imports	"	491	697	a
Exports	"	98,852	117,391	a
World production (approximate)	"	127,000	a	a

[a] Figures not yet available.
[b] Excludes "All other manufactures of nickel"; weight not recorded.
[c] Excludes "Manufactures"; weight not recorded.
[d] Price quoted by International Nickel Co. of Canada, Ltd., for electrolytic nickel at New York, in 2-ton minimum lots.

All mines and smelters of the International Nickel Company operated at capacity throughout 1941, according to a report of Robert S. Stanley, President, and an expansion program was inaugurated which will, when completed in 1943, increase capacity 50,000,000 pounds a year over the 1940 rate.

Large low-grade deposits of nickel have been discovered in Cuba, and very recently the War Production Board approved a project involving the expenditure of about $20,000,000 for the construction of a plant and facilities for the recovery of the metal from the ores.

Also, by emergency adaptions of existing equipment in this country and alterations and extensions, provision is being made for the treatment of intermediate products and for additional supplies of nickel.

Meanwhile, despite the large increase in our imports in 1940, so much nickel was needed that year to meet the requirements of the defense program, plus regular commercial uses, that several times a

NICKEL

WORLD PRODUCTION 1938

CANADA

NEW CALEDONIA

OTHER COUNTRIES

EACH REPRESENTS 10,000 METRIC TONS

tight situation in supply developed. Consequently, on March 7, 1941, all supplies of nickel were put under priority control, making it possible for the Priorities Division and the industry to facilitate a steady flow of the metal into factories working on both British and Canadian orders and those for our own Army and Navy.

Despite all efforts, 1940 witnessed little or no improvement in our domestic production. The search for commercial deposits in this country was continued and a few projects were started. The Cobalt Gold Mining Company is working on ore today, at Gold Hill, Colorado, containing about 3 percent nickel with lesser amounts of cobalt and copper, and it has built a smelter expected to produce a matte containing 45 to 55 percent nickel. The amount of nickel that can be so produced was not mentioned in the Minerals Year Book for 1940. It is undoubtedly small, as was that of a concentrate containing 20 percent nickel reported by the Magnesia Talc Company from their plant located in Vermont.

Such projects as these make no real change in our situation with regard to nickel—which remains strategically sound due to the assurance of continuous supplies from Canada.

Tungsten

Tungsten is a Swedish word meaning "heavy stone," the name originally given to the ore from which the Swedish chemist, C. W. Scheele, first produced tungstic acid in 1781. Two years later, when the metal itself was isolated by the brothers Elhujas, they dubbed the ore "Scheelite" and applied the term tungsten to the element.

Scheelite is really calcium tungstate—a salt of tungstic acid—and is now not widely used. The principal tungsten ore today is wolframite, a tungstate of iron and manganese which contains about 60 percent of tungsten.

It was a British scientist who, in the nineteenth century, first reduced the tungsten ore to the iron-tungsten alloy which is at present the most useful compound and the form in which tungsten is most important; the pure metal has comparatively few applications.

Ferro-tungsten, containing 75 to 80 percent of tungsten, is produced in the electric furnace from high-grade concentrates—ore from which most foreign elements have been removed. By the addition of definite amounts of ferro-tungsten to the steel bath containing chromium and vanadium an alloy is produced with a tungsten content of 15 to 20 percent.

This metal gives steel a relatively high melting-point besides making it both harder and tougher. These are the qualities which make tungsten steels particularly suited for high-speed cutting tools, and for all of them reasonably pure tungsten metal must be used. One such steel, containing chromium and cobalt as well as tungsten, is stellite, which has various modifications but is essentially used to keep the cutting edges sharp at very high temperatures. Then there are the carballoys, belonging to the carbide series, which give the fastest cutting edge so far developed.

Since the majority of machine parts and castings require just such toolings in the process of their manufacture, tungsten steels play a tremendously important part in modern mass production, and as the latter is, in turn, indispensable in the prosecution of modern mechanized warfare, tungsten has very definite strategic significance.

There are, also, several strictly military applications of this element. Tungsten alloy steels are used for armor-piercing munitions, as cores for light arms, in the manufacture of armor-plate, and as erosion-resistance liners in heavy ordnance.

The principal peacetime application of tungsten (aside from steel which is basic to our modern life) and the only one in which the pure metal is widely used is in the filaments of electric light bulbs and radio tubes. Such a minute amount of tungsten is used for each one that it takes less than a hundred tons of it to produce all the millions of bulbs and radio tubes manufactured in this country every year. If it were necessary, however, to produce in the old way the light and heat generated in these bulbs and tubes the cost would be multiplied not hundreds but thousands of times. Those of us who can remember the old type of carbon electric light bulbs will recall that they cost several times as much as those we buy today and that they lasted about one-tenth as long. Tantalum is the only substitute for tungsten for such use, and it is not nearly as satisfactory.

Tungsten is also used in hard facing alloys which have an infinite number of applications, including oil-drill bits and the treads of tractors.

While far from being as general as the uses of tungsten discussed above, the presence of sodium tungstate as a pigment in paints, textiles and rubber is nevertheless worth mentioning. In this case the tungsten has the quality of absorbing dyes and fixing colors—giving a high brilliancy to the dyed product as well as strong resistance to light. Similarly, sodium tungstate is used to fireproof both textiles and wood.

In normal times we consume about 4,500 to 5,000 short tons of tungsten a year, and produce about half of that amount. In the first four months of 1941, however, we were using tungsten at the rate of 10,200 net tons a year and this tempo was doubtless doubled by the end of the year. Domestic production cannot be increased appreciably for some time.

Some of our western states have fairly large deposits of the ore—especially Nevada, California and Colorado. They have been responsible for about 90 percent of our domestic output. Recent tests by experts of the Westinghouse Company have shown that wolframite from Washington, South Dakota, Idaho and Arizona also yields satisfactory tungsten and these deposits may be exploited.

Large-scale production, however, cannot be achieved at once, and for our immediate needs we must depend on imports; although shipments of tungsten concentrates from United States mines reached 5,319 short tons in 1940, an increase of 24 percent over 1939.

Imports for consumption in 1940 were also tremendously increased —almost four times their volume in 1939; and in spite of the difficulties in moving Chinese tungsten we received from that country three times as much of the metal as the year before.

Normally, the bulk, about 80 percent, of the ore we import comes from China, which is the world's leading producer of tungsten (with India and the United States rather poor second and third) principally because of the cheap labor available in that country. Shipments from there fell substantially the last few years due to the Sino-Japanese war, but the Chinese have been making every effort to send us the ores we need. They managed to ship us 1,717 tons in 1940 and 1,233 tons in January and March of 1941. Moreover since early 1941 all exports shipped over the Burma Road have been exclusively for the United States, with small exceptions sent to Shanghai and the Straits.

Besides the ore imports from China, in normal times we bought small amounts of metal and alloys from England, Germany and Holland, and ore from Chile, Peru and Bolivia which promises some day to rival China as a tungsten producer. At present its established capacity is only about 4,000 short tons a year, but its potential annual output has been reliably estimated at well over twice that amount.

In May, 1941, the Metals Reserve Company (subsidiary of the RFC) announced that it had contracted with Bolivian producers, under Government guarantees, to purchase their entire production of tungsten for the next three years. About $24,000,000 is expected to be involved in the total contract, with around 4,400 tons of tungsten oxide being shipped each year. American consumers will be allowed to purchase the ore they need at approximately the market price, except for such quantities as the MRC may set aside for Government stock piles.

Besides these efforts to build up a new source of supply in Bolivia, we are investigating the possibilities in Peru and Argentina, and several tons of tungsten from the latter country are now being used by the Westinghouse Lamp Company on an experimental basis.

In fact, during 1940 the aggregate of the imports of tungsten from Argentina, Bolivia, Brazil, Chile, Cuba, Mexico and Peru amounted to 3,362,778 pounds (tungsten content), or more than the total general imports from all sources in 1939.

Let us consider now our present situation with regard to tungsten. On the basis of a war requirement of 60,000,000 tons of steel a year, we need about 9,500 short tons of metallic tungsten—calculated on the ratio of 15 pounds of tungsten per ton of steel—or 19,000 short tons for two years.

While this figure is several times that of our normal rate of production it need not frighten us. First, because it is possible to use substitutes for tungsten in several of its more important applications. In the case of electric light bulbs, for instance, while it would be both expensive and inconvenient to go back to the old carbon filament, it could be done if absolutely necessary.

Zirconium is reportedly being used as a substitute in armor-piercing bullets, as well as in cutting tools when alloyed with nickel. Indeed, not only has research on alloy substitutes reached an advanced stage of development, but also the continuous progress being made in increasing the velocity of small armor-piercing bullets may put both tungsten and its substitute completely out of the picture.

All this, however, is still in the future. What we are sure of is the fact that the use of molybdenum could cut our tungsten consumption in half; for molybdenum has been proved to be a satisfactory substitute in high-speed steels. In fact, the first order issued by the Office of Production Management in which a substitute material was specifically required was that published on June 12, 1941, asking buyers of high-speed tools to specify molybdenum instead of tungsten in orders where it was possible to use a molybdenum type of steel. Those who do buy tungsten steel must purchase an equal amount of the other over a three-month period.

Such conservation is intended to bring our two-year wartime requirement of tungsten down to 9,500 short tons.

It is believed that our domestic production can be placed on an annual basis of 6,000 short tons, equal to 12,000 short tons for two years, or more than we would require; while at a high price our domestic mines could produce as much as 18,000 short tons, so that we would not even need to substitute molybdenum. All this, of course, is based on an emergency which would make it impossible for us to import from South America; and that is certainly not likely to be the case.

Moreover, the Government has been laying in a stock pile of tungsten for the past two years, under the authority of the Strategic Materials Act of 1939. In June of 1940 it became known that there was a large tonnage of Chinese tungsten ore at the ports of Haiphong and Saigon, Indo-China, intended by the Chinese Government for shipment to the United States, but in imminent danger of seizure by the

Japanese. Our authorities moved very quickly. The Reconstruction Finance Corporation immediately agreed to purchase all available ore from Indo-China; space was obtained on two American ships and their clearance procured—with the result that within two weeks of the reception in Washington of the news the ore was on its way to this country.

Some months later, the Metals Reserve Company arranged to accept $30,000,000 worth of tungsten from China (to be delivered over a period of years) in payment for a loan by the Export-Import Bank; and still more recently another loan of $60,000,000 was arranged to be repaid by sales of tungsten, antimony, and pig tin.

Consequently, our strategic situation with regard to tungsten is really highly favorable. As late as the end of 1941 we were receiving ore from China. Latin America is becoming an increasingly important source of the metal. And we can, if necessary, do without imports altogether.

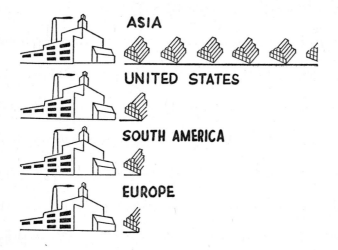

TUNGSTEN ORE
WORLD PRODUCTION 1937

ASIA

UNITED STATES

SOUTH AMERICA

EUROPE

EACH REPRESENTS 5,000 METRIC TONS

Salient Statistics of the Tungsten Industry
in the United States, 1939-40

	1939		1940	
	Short Tons	*Value*	*Short Tons*	*Value*
Production (60 percent WO₃)	3,603	a	5,120	a
Concentrates shipped (60 percent WO₃)	4,287	$4,402,182	5,319	$6,576,318
Imported for consumption (W content)	743	997,971	2,805	4,690,723
Stocks in bonded warehouses, Dec. 31:				
Ore (W content)	843	1,357,219	2,196	3,956,825
Metal (W content)	6	14,975	7	23,587

a Figures not available.

Tungsten Ore and Concentrates Imported for Consumption
in the United States, 1939-40, by Countries

	1939			1940		
	Gross Weight (pounds)	*Tungsten Content (pounds)*	*Value*	*Gross Weight (pounds)*	*Tungsten Content (pounds)*	*Value*
Africa:						
Union of South Africa				102,577	53,511	$47,325
Other British South Africa				142	73	65
Argentina	141,872	76,524	$50,324	1,450,424	762,012	632,484
Australia	102,216	56,639	42,196	1,017,236	573,038	479,944
Bolivia	180,019	96,164	77,342	2,523,354	1,208,595	970,251
British Malaya	200,843	123,682	113,063	274,847	162,783	167,671
Burma	24,576	12,878	8,683	175,225	93,549	71,759
Chile				4,409	2,469	1,697
China	1,656,307	899,806	587,489	3,634,563	1,899,526	1,670,085
Cuba				5,092	2,781	3,810
Ecuador	37,440	21,326	7,500			
French Indo-China	5,630	2,876	2,832	47,710	14,417	14,459
India, British				53,943	30,000	25,486
Mexico	306,907	146,637	89,352	217,430	113,867	71,823
Peru	87,662	48,625	19,190	369,885	174,893	129,579
Portugal				598,172	322,681	273,244
Thailand				354,084	196,687	131,041
	2,743,472	1,485,157	997,971	10,829,093	5,610,882	4,690,723

TUNGSTEN ORE

IMPORTED INTO THE UNITED STATES 1940

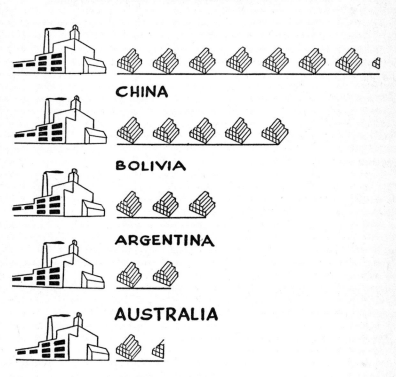

CHINA

BOLIVIA

ARGENTINA

AUSTRALIA

PORTUGAL

EACH 🔲 REPRESENTS 250 METRIC TONS

Vanadium

There are over fifty minerals containing vanadium, one of the most widely distributed of the metals. Only a few, however, are found in quantities sufficient to be of commercial value; and of the four principal ores—carnotite, patronite, roscoelite and vanadinite—the first two are the most important, one of them containing radium and uranium, the other vanadium sulfide.

Vanadium is an essential raw material in any industrial country at peace or at war, for it is an alloying element valuable in the manufacture of steel. It produces much the same effect as nickel, with the important difference that much smaller amounts of vanadium are required—seldom more than 4 percent. Added to steel in the form of ferrovanadium, it controls the growth of grain in the steel.

Chrome-vanadium steels play a vital part in the manufacture of driving axles and other forgings of locomotives, auto-springs and transmission axles and gun forgings. Vanadium is also an essential component in the making of steels for the high-speed tools which are necessary to mass production, and other vanadium steels are used in armor-plate.

About 95 percent of the total vanadium produced is, consequently, used in the making of steel. The rest finds its way into a variety of products, mostly chemical. In the contact process for manufacturing sulfuric acid, for instance, and in making certain organic chemicals, the use of vanadium as a catalyst seems to be increasing, but a few tons a year will still suffice for these products. It is also employed in salts to color pottery and glass, and as a mordant in dyeing.

World production of vanadium for 1939 amounted to 2,962 metric tons, of which Peru contributed 1,016 tons, the United States 900, Southwest Africa 514, Northern Rhodesia 384, and Mexico 148.

Peruvian output, all from the Minasagra mine, was increased in 1940 by more than 25 percent, and our production was increased to 948 metric tons, most of which came from Colorado, where the United States Vanadium Corporation has extensive mining operations.

Arizona, New Mexico and Utah also contain vanadium-bearing ores, some of which are now being mined; and the Anaconda Copper Mining Company is planning to produce vanadium as a by-product.

Apparent domestic consumption in 1940 was approximately 3,000,-

000 pounds; for 1941 5,900,000 pounds. Requirements for 1942 were expected to reach 7,150,000 pounds.

The extent of our domestic reserves is not known, so that possible production in this country cannot be estimated. It is doubtful, however, that we could meet emergency needs without imports from Peru.

That is why in August of 1941 the metal was placed under full priority control.

Salient Statistics of the Vanadium Industry in the United States, 1939-40

		1939		1940	
		Quantity	Value	Quantity	Value
Shipments:					
Carnotite ores	short tons	6,256	$174,660	796[a]	$ 61,800[a]
Vanadium contained	pounds	206,509	[b]	51,377	[b]
Uranium contained	"	59,269	[b]	16,909	[b]
Vanadium ores	short tons	273,098[c]	879,000[cd]	95,549	968,000[de]
Vanadium contained	pounds	1,777,559[f]	—	2,015,729	—
By-product salt from complex ores:					
vanadium contained	pounds	[b]	[b]	23,495	[e]
Imports:					
Vanadium ores	short tons	15,694	991,511	22,551	1,216,705
Vanadium contained	pounds	2,132,548	—	2,574,951	—

[a] Includes only ore sold for uranium and vanadium values; ore sold only for its vanadium value included with vanadium ores.

[b] Figures not available.

[c] Includes complex ores.

[d] Estimated by Bureau of Mines.

[e] Value of vanadium contained in by-product salt from complex ores included with value of vanadium ores.

[f] Includes vanadium content of complex ores.

VANADIUM ORE
WORLD PRODUCTION 1939

PERU

UNITED STATES

SOUTHWEST AFRICA

NORTHERN RHODESIA

MEXICO

EACH REPRESENTS 150 METRIC TONS

[3]

Other Vital Members of the War Machine

MONG all the strategic and critical raw materials not necessary in the
roduction of steel aluminum is probably the most vital to our war
fort, since adequate plane production depends so largely upon suf-
cient supplies of this metal. It is, therefore, very fortunate for us that
rge bauxite deposits exist in the Western Hemisphere—deposits now
uarded by the United States Marines.

As for the remaining materials essential to the armament program
nd not normally produced in sufficient quantity at home, no one of
em can really be said to be more important than any other. Asbestos
necessary in all mechanical equipment; antimony and mercury are
eeded for ammunition; platinum, mica and quartz crystal play
tally important parts in electrical and radio equipment; optical
ass must be had for precision instruments; toluol and phenol go
to the manufacture of a great many explosives.

Some of these materials—such as asbestos and platinum—offer no
rious procurement problem because of large deposits in Canada;
hers are a little more difficult to secure, since they must come from
uth America; for others the question is simply one of increased
mestic production. However, all of them, as well as the peacetime
roducts in which they are used, will be hard to obtain for the duration.

Aluminum

While aluminum is the most abundant of all the metals in the
rth's crust, it is among the most difficult to obtain in usable form.
the first place, this metal never occurs free, and to be useful to man
must be separated from the other elements in the various compounds

in which it is found; and most of these contain only slight amount
of aluminum. Bauxite is the only one, in fact, commonly used to pro
duce the metal.

Named for the town of Les Baux in southern France, where it was
first discovered, this ore usually contains about 55 percent aluminum
oxide, which it yields only under protest, so to speak, and from which
aluminum itself must then be extracted.

In fact, this metal probably would still be the chemical curiosity i
remained for fifty years after its discovery but for the brilliant young
American chemist, Charles Martin Hall, who first dissolved aluminum
oxide in a fused bath of cryolite and then passed an electric curren
through it to produce pure aluminum. Before his discovery sodium
had to be used as a reducing agent in a chemical process so expensiv
that the metal sold for $8 a pound. Today aluminum sells for 15 cent
a pound.

Even with the electrolytic process it is not cheap to produce. It take
two tons of bauxite and two of coal, or other fuel, and about 20
pounds of soda ash to procure one ton of alumina (the oxide) by th
Bayer process, a combination of a chemical and roasting treatment
and about 20,000 to 24,000 kilowatt hours of electric energy are the
required to produce a ton of aluminum from the oxide. That is wh
southern France was until recently the leading producer of bauxite
for fuel and power are cheap there, the ore deposits are all within
radius of a few hundred miles, and the aluminum oxide content o
the ores is potentially high.

Hall lived to see the price of aluminum come down from dollars t
cents a pound, but he never dreamed what far-reaching results thi
difference in price would make. In fact, he was "frightened" whe
the "tremendous" amount of 50 pounds of aluminum was first pro
duced in one day in a Pittsburgh plant.

In 1939 the world production of aluminum had risen to over 647,00
metric tons a year. The United States that year produced 327,000,00
pounds, and this metal, first cast in the form of a homely teapot, ha
become an essential war material. This was not because of uses ex
clusively or even specifically military but because of a peculiar com
bination of properties making it useful in such a great variety of ways

Kitchen utensils and other everyday things, such as bottle-caps an
toothpaste tubes, as well as equipment for handling milk and beer
are made of aluminum because of the metal's resistance to corrosio

and its lightness. It is this characteristic of lightness plus high strength that count in the various types of transportation equipment for which aluminum is used—trains, street-cars, aircraft, truck bodies, tank cars, mine-cages, bridge-floors, and many other things. All three properties—corrosion-resistance, lightness and strength—are important in plane and dirigible construction.

Aluminum in normal times is widely employed in foil and paint—the foil for wrapping food products and as a heat insulator, and the paint for outdoor storage tanks because of its ability to reflect heat and cut down volatilization losses.

As a deoxidation agent aluminum metal is used in appreciable amounts, and this is important because in this way the metal is completely consumed whereas in most other uses it is added to the pool of secondary reserves.

Bauxite, as such, is the raw material for abrasives, refractories and a special type of alumina cement which is capable of developing its maximum strength faster than Portland cement and which can resist both relatively high temperatures and chemical attack.

Aluminum chemicals take about 15 to 20 percent of the domestic bauxite supply for use in water purification, paper-making, dyeing, and petroleum refining.

For some of these applications there can be no substitutes, since no other metal has the peculiar combination of properties characteristic of aluminum. In many commercial applications, however, aluminum is a convenience and not a necessity and in the war emergency has already been replaced in some instances. Unfortunately, in those uses which are of primary military importance—such as the construction of fighter or bombing planes—where the combination of lightness and strength is essential, not only is aluminum irreplaceable but only the best grades of primary metal can be used.

That is the principal reason why aluminum is on the priority list—not because we do not have enough bauxite in this country, but because our deposits are chiefly of low-grade ore from which it is expensive to procure large amounts of pure metal.

Until very recently most of our domestic production of aluminum was of secondary metal, and only enough bauxite was mined in this country to supply about three-fourths of the aluminum needs of the chemical industry. At least half of our annual consumption was imported.

Now the situation is very different; our bauxite reserves are to
fully exploited and they are considerable. Recent estimates of t
Bureau of Mines and other investigators indicate that the State
Arkansas, where the chief deposits are found, contains about 8,500,0
tons of high-grade and 15,000,000 tons of low-grade ore.

Two new plants are being built in that state, each to produ
500,000,000 pounds of alumina a year, using the low-grade ores nev
before considered to have any commercial value, thereby tripling o
useful reserves of bauxite. Financed by the Defense Plant Corporatio
these plants are to be built and operated by the Aluminum Compa:
of America (Alcoa); but in the case of the second one to be bui
the Government will probably retain ownership of the alumina pr
duced and sell it to smaller aluminum-making companies with 1
raw material supplies of their own.

These are but two of the many new additions to the productic
facilities of Alcoa. Down in Surinam (Dutch Guiana) where th
own extensive bauxite deposits, now guarded by U. S. Marines, a ne
mine and mill have been opened up with a combined capacity
250 tons of dried bauxite an hour; and ten old and two new vess
have been bought to facilitate shipments of this ore to the Unit
States.

The entire bauxite production of Dutch Guiana has long be
exported to this country, for Alcoa, through a subsidiary, has alwa
been the only producer. In the past only one mine was in operatio
shipping around 600,000 tons a year at the most. This amount can no
be more than doubled even if the new plant and mine work on
eight hours a day, six days a week.

These increased shipments of bauxite by the Surinam subsidia
are being taken care of in the new self-financed plants recently co
structed by the Aluminum Company of America at a cost of $20(
000,000. Located on the Columbia River near Vancouver, Washingto
one aluminum plant which was started early in the spring of 1940 w
five months later producing at an annual rate of 30,000,000 pounds
year, and by May of 1941 that output had been multiplied five tim
and will be similarly increased during 1942.

It has also been announced by the Defense Plant Corporation th.
Alcoa will build and operate a second plant in the Portland, Orego:
district with an annual capacity of 90,000,000 pounds, as well :

ding 150,000,000 pounds of smelting capacity at Massena, New York, d constructing a metal plant in Arkansas.

Besides these and several other aluminum plants being built by lcoa and the expansion of existing facilities, this company has also eatly increased the capacity of its manufacturing units.

The total result of all this activity was a production in 1941, by the uminum Company of America alone, of nearly 600,000,000 pounds aluminum, which will be increased to 760,000,000 pounds by July, 42.

In addition to Alcoa's tremendous contribution to our aluminum eds is the production of a company new in this field, Reynolds etals. Granted an industrial expansion loan of $15,800,000 by the ?C in July, 1940, this company began construction in November of it year on plants at Lister, Alabama, capable of producing 100,000 ort tons of alumina and 30,000 tons of aluminum a year. And with additional loan of $4,200,000 a reduction plant at Longview, Wash- ;ton, was constructed to take care of the alumina produced at Lister, nging the total annual aluminum production of the company up 50,000 tons.

Bauxite for Reynolds Metals has come from the Netherlands Indies d Brazil as well as from British Guiana. Intense development is w going on in the latter country to increase the output of the ore to et the needs of the Canadian counterpart of Alcoa, to which most this production will go, and our own increased demands.

Another interesting new development in the aluminum field is a ocess, recently developed, which will make it possible to produce minum metal from the large reserves (about 13,788,675 tons, ac- ding to the Bureau of Mines) of alunite now lying idle in Utah, izona, Colorado, California, Nevada and Washington. In Utah ne, where the new process was developed by Arthur Fleischer, of lunite, Inc., at least 3,800,000 tons of pure alunite are available, uring a life of at least ten years to a plant producing 200 tons a day t an estimated production cost of 11.865 cents per pound of minum.

In August of 1941 the OPM recommended to the War Department it operations be started on a small scale at Marysvale, Utah, and ried on by Kalunite, Inc. As a start, a plant having a capacity of tons of ore a day was to be built. The company was asked also to gage in the experimental treatment of aluminous clays which exist in much greater quantities than any other aluminous minerals in thi country.

At that time it was announced that when all plants recommende by the Government were in operation, the total alumina capacity the United States would be 2,720,000 pounds a year, within 400,000,0

World Production of Bauxite, 1936-40, by Countries, in Metric Tons

(*Compiled by L. P. Lounsbery*)

COUNTRY	1936	1937	1938	1939	1940
Australia:					
New South Wales	—	6,793	442	a	a
Victoria	752	1,097	1,341	820	1,00
Brazil (exports)	7,000	8,770	12,928	18,279	20,00
Czechoslovakia	—	846	a	a	a
France	649,500	688,200	682,440	800,000[b]	700,00
Germany	12,425	18,212	19,703	20,000[b]	20,00
Greece	129,898	137,412	179,886	186,906	50,00
Guiana:					
British	172,884	305,533	382,409	483,653	700,00
Dutch (Surinam)	234,845	392,447	377,213	511,619	615,43
Hungary	329,091	532,657	540,718	485,000	700,00
India, British	3,702	15,393	15,005	9,121	15,00
Indo-China	30	7,000	160	330	11
Italy	262,246	386,495	360,837	483,965	530,00
Netherlands Indies	133,731	198,970	245,354	230,668	274,34
Portuguese East Africa	29	—	—	180	a
Rumania	10,829	10,701	11,807	10,460	40,00
Unfederated Malay States:					
Johore	37	19,305	55,965	93,737	63,78
U.S.S.R.	203,200	230,000[b]	250,000[b]	270,000[b]	300,00
United States (dried bauxite equivalent)	386,415	431,898	315,906	381,331	445,95
Yugoslavia	292,174	354,233	396,368	318,840	150,00
	2,829,000	3,746,000	3,849,000	4,306,000[b]	4,627,00

[a] Data not available.
[b] Estimated production.

pounds of the amount then considered necessary to produce 1,400,00 000 pounds of aluminum metal a year, besides meeting the alumir requirements of the abrasives and chemical industries.

Bauxite was then being imported from Dutch Guiana at the rate 1,300,000 tons a year and it was estimated that production of the o in Arkansas would amount to over 2,000,000 tons a year.

Since then we have entered the war and the demand for planes and planes and still more planes grows more insistent every day. Now the top rate of production is set at 2,100,000 pounds a year.

Each of the heavy bombers we build—and we hope to produce 10,000 of them a year—requires 30,000 pounds of aluminum; each of the fighter planes 5,000 pounds. At a yearly production of 50,000 fighter planes (to be doubled in 1943) we will need 500,000,000 pounds of aluminum a year for these two items alone.

Even if we produce the 1,400,000 pounds of aluminum hoped for by the end of 1942 it will still be necessary to make use of every available substitute, and it is fortunate that several of these exist.

To make the "flivver" or spin-proof type of plane used for training purposes, steel and a light wood (such as balsa wood from Ecuador) or plastic-bound plywood will suffice. And plastics now replace aluminum in several airplane parts—cowl covers, engine baffles and flooring, trim and control tabs as well as supports, shelves, seats and so forth, in planes not subject to great strain.

Steel forgings, steel, iron or lead castings, laminated plastics, may be used instead of aluminum casting.

For aluminum foil, oiled paper, glassine, lead foil may be substituted. For aluminum paint, one with a titanium base and a special penetrating oil may be used.

Plastics, steel, or porcelain enamel, could replace aluminum in many of the uses with which we are most familiar—cooking utensils, washing-machine parts, refrigerator parts, thermos bottles, etc.; even for some radio parts; but in electrolytic condensers aluminum alone will do.

The result will be a decided change in the appearance—we trust not in the efficiency—of many familiar objects. Americans, so fond of shiny gadgets, are going to have to do without many of them in order to "keep them flying."

Salient Statistics of the Bauxite and Aluminum Industries in the United States, 1938-40

		1938	1939	1940
Bauxite:				
Production (mine shipments)[a]	Long tons	310,916	375,307	438,913
Value [b]		$ 1,812,545	$ 2,166,236	$ 2,578,968
Imports [b]	Long tons	455,693	520,179	629,552
Exports (including concentrates)[b]	Long tons	57,726	51,635	81,913
World production	Long tons	3,788,000	4,238,000	4,554,000
Aluminum:				
Primary production	Short tons	143,441	163,545	206,280
Value		$56,659,000	$64,600,000	$75,292,000
Quoted price per pound [d]	cents	20.0	20.0	18.7
Secondary production	Short tons	38,800	50,000	[e]
Imports		$ 3,379,018	$ 4,766,260	$ 5,159,924
Exports		$ 5,484,047	$23,705,250	$22,437,125
World production	Short tons	638,000	735,000[c]	885,000

[a] Dried bauxite equivalent.
[b] As shipped.
[c] Estimated.
[d] New York: 99 percent plus, pure virgin ingot, according to Metal Statistics 1941, published by American Metal Market.
[e] Figures not available.

World Production of Aluminum, 1936-40, by Countries, in Metric Tons

(Compiled by L. P. Lounsbery)

	1936	1937	1938	1939	1940
Canada	26,200	41,700	66,000	75,000	110,000
France	29,700	34,500	45,300	50,000	50,000
Germany	97,200	127,200	161,100	200,000[a]	240,000
Austria	3,300	4,400	4,500		
Hungary	800	1,000	1,500	1,500	2,800
Italy	15,900	22,900	25,800	34,200	40,000
Japan	7,000	10,000	17,000	23,000	35,000
Norway	15,400	23,000	29,000	31,000	15,000
Spain	600	—	800	800[a]	500
Sweden	1,800	1,800	2,400	2,700	1,400
Switzerland	13,700	25,000	27,000	28,000	28,000
U.S.S.R.	30,000	37,700	43,800	45,000[a]	55,000
United Kingdom	16,300	19,300	23,300	25,000	35,000
United States	102,000	132,800	130,100	148,400	187,100
Yugoslavia	—	200	1,200	2,400	2,800
	359,900	481,500	578,800	667,000	803,000

[a] Estimated production.

ALUMINUM
WORLD PRODUCTION - 1940

EUROPE
380,500 METRIC TONS

NORTH AMERICA
297,000 METRIC TONS

RUSSIA
55,000 METRIC TONS

ASIA
35,000 METRIC TONS

Asbestos

Speak of asbestos and we think of the fire-drop curtain in a theatre. Asbestos is not the name of a single element, but a common term applied to several minerals, differing widely in chemical composition and in certain physical characteristics, but alike in that they are capable of being worked into flexible fibers that can be spun into yarns or woven into cloths that are non-inflammable and only slightly reactive to acids.

These peculiar properties of certain fibrous minerals have been known for many centuries. The ancient Romans used asbestos in winding-sheets for the cremation of their dead. Charlemagne used asbestos cloth as a means of mystifying people he wanted to impress— he would toss a strip of the material into a blazing fire, proving to the ignorant onlookers that he had bewitched the cloth so that it could not burn. Marco Polo was shown a non-inflammable material on his way through Siberia; and in 1676 Chinese merchants demonstrated asbestos handkerchiefs to the Royal Society of London.

Some time later asbestos was discovered in the Ural Mountains, and during the reign of Peter the Great the first factory for making asbestos articles was operated in Russia; but known uses were so few and demand so small that the industry subsequently disappeared.

After that asbestos was forgotten until about 1808, when an Italian lady of noble rank became interested and sponsored studies and experiments leading to the manufacture of asbestos thread, fabrics and paper of high quality.

Several companies were formed in Italy between 1860 and 1875, but they had great difficulty in devising machinery for spinning the fibers. Nevertheless, their products attracted a great deal of attention at the Paris Exposition of 1876.

The very next year large deposits of asbestos were discovered in Canada and mining began in 1878 with a production of 50 tons, which was increased to 1,400 in seven years. By that time there was a growing market in the United States for asbestos products, but it was not until 1915, when mechanical methods of fiber recovery were introduced, that the industry felt its first great spurt.

The development of the automobile, too, had a great deal to do with the growth of the asbestos industry. There was no such demand for fireproof garments and asbestos theatre curtains as was created by the use of this material for brake linings and clutch facings in cars. The first type used, and still important today, is brake linings formed from asbestos cloth. But even in the molded linings, used on some passenger cars, asbestos is an essential ingredient. No other material possesses the combination of characteristics necessary to withstand the terrific heat created by friction when the brakes are applied on today's high-speed cars. Much industrial equipment, too, depends upon clutches and brakes lined with asbestos. Power shovels, hoists, tractors, derricks, trucks, fly-wheels, and winders are a few. Asbestos packings and gaskets, also, are important to the efficient operation of engines and machines.

Theatre curtains and some scenery and awnings are made of asbestos cloth; and in factories it is used for conveyor belts carrying hot materials.

Another use that is conserving fuel and saving money in both home and industry is asbestos insulation. Combined with 85 percent magnesia, it forms an insulation for temperatures to 600 degrees F.; combined with diatomaceous silica, it forms an insulation for higher temperatures, to 1900 degrees F.—two important heat savers in industrial operations. Felted into sheets and cylindrical sections, it is used to cover hot surfaces and pipes in homes. Asbestos felts are also used to reduce fire hazard around stoves and as a sheeting between the floors of a building, as well as in many household appliances. Impregnated with asphalt, asbestos felts are widely used as a roof surfacing.

Within the past twenty-five years asbestos has been combined with cement to produce a great number of very useful products. In flat and corrugated sheets, cement-asbestos products are used for roofs and side walls for industrial buildings, hangars, warehouses, and other structures. These sheets are quickly erected, afford great weather resistance, and need no painting to preserve them. With decorative finishes, the flat sheets are used for office partitions.

Thousands of miles of pipes made of asbestos and cement are being used throughout the world to carry water and sewage and to vent domestic gas appliances and industrial fumes. Additional miles of the material are used as conduit to carry electrical cables.

In the home, panels of cement-asbestos composition with decorative finishes are used for colorful and durable walls in kitchens and bath-rooms. Thousands of homes are protected from roof-communicated fires with roofs of asbestos shingles.

However, the market for asbestos depends not only on the auto-mobile and building trades but on many other industries as well; so it is not surprising that we are the largest consumers of this material (using about 250,000 short tons a year) and lead all countries in the manufacture of asbestos products. We export every year nearly half the ten million dollars' worth of asbestos we usually import, not in-cluding that which has been used in finished products, such as auto-mobiles which we export.

We produce, however, less than 8 percent of the amount we use, even now with domestic output at an all-time high, and it is fortunate for us that Canada, in the southern part of Quebec, has the world's largest deposits of asbestos, for we depend almost entirely upon that country for our supplies, taking nearly 75 percent of the Canadian output. And as Canada has lost her continental European asbestos markets, there is no shortage of the supply available for our needs.

The other large producers in the world are Rhodesia, South Africa, Russia and Cyprus, though there are asbestos deposits in at least eighteen other countries, including three in South America—Argen-tina, Bolivia and Venezuela. African imports into this country have been increasing in spite of the war. In fact, we received over 17,000 short tons of asbestos from Africa in 1940—54 percent more than in 1939.

We have scattered deposits in California and other western states, especially Arizona, and more extensive beds in Vermont. Our total production while still less than 25,000 short tons, is being greatly increased because of the emergency.

If necessary, we can also use substitutes in certain types of con-struction work, replacing asbestos insulating materials with mineral or glass wool. While they lack some of the flexibility and strength of asbestos, they have its more important properties. In this way we can release stocks of asbestos large enough, with our domestic production, to cover our essential munitions needs—automobile brake linings, packing and gaskets, and certain insulating materials.

Therefore our strategic position with regard to asbestos is extremely favorable, and this material is on the critical list only as a precautionary measure.

ASBESTOS
IMPORTED INTO THE UNITED STATES 1940

CANADA

OTHER COUNTRIES

EACH ⊟ REPRESENTS 20,000 SHORT TONS

Salient Statistics of the Asbestos Industry in the United States, 1939-40

	1939		1940	
	Short Tons	Value	Short Tons	Value
Domestic asbestos				
Produced:				
Chrysotile	14,686	a	17,481	a
Amphibole	450	a	1,693	a
Total produced	15,136	a	19,174	a
Sold or used by producers:				
Chrysotile	15,043	$503,097	18,672	$664,520
Amphibole	416	9,691	1,388	9,988
Total sold or used by producers	15,459	512,788	20,060	674,508
Imports (unmanufactured)	242,561	9,094,538	246,613	10,034,433
Exports (unmanufactured)	2,473	218,830	4,474	449,105
Apparent consumption [b]	255,547	9,388,496	262,199	10,259,836
Exports of asbestos products	a	3,354,920	a	3,473,246

[a] Figures not available.
[b] Quantity sold or used by producers, plus imports, minus exports.

Asbestos (unmanufactured) Imported for Consumption in the United States, 1939-40, by Countries and Classes

	CRUDE (including blue fiber)		MILL FIBERS	
	Short Tons	Value	Short Tons	Value
1939				
Africa:				
Union of South Africa	6,359	$656,543	—	—
"Other British"	4,836	593,596	—	—
Australia	53	11,000	—	—
Canada	3,068	547,425	73,511	$4,378,887
Finland	—	—	—	—
Italy	31	23,167	—	—
Malta, Gozo, Cyprus	—	—	—	—
U.S.S.R.	—	—	2,611	109,516
United Kingdom	298	40,580	—	—
Venezuela	—	—	—	—
	14,645	1,872,311	76,122	4,488,403
1940				
Africa:				
Union of South Africa	8,752	835,649	—	—
"Other British"	8,462	1,005,844	—	—
Australia	28	7,569	—	—
Bolivia	1	118	—	—
Canada	1,572	400,501	81,631	4,960,416
India, British	1	647	—	—
Italy	17	13,031	—	—
Malta, Gozo, Cyprus	—	—	—	—
Netherlands Indies	19	1,738	—	—
United Kingdom	18	3,239	—	—
Venezuela	—	—	—	—
	18,870	2,268,336	81,631	4,960,416

[a] Asbestos, n.e.s., containing not over 15 percent of foreign matter.
[b] Less than 1 ton.

Asbestos (unmanufactured) Imported for Consumption
in the United States, 1939-40, by Countries and Classes (*continued*)

| SHORT FIBERS [a] | | TOTAL | |
Short Tons	Value	Short Tons	Value
—	—	6,359	$656,543
—	—	4,836	593,596
—	—	53	11,000
147,261	$2,650,886	223,840	7,577,198
46	1,324	46	1,324
536	12,133	567	35,300
3,940	69,426	3,940	69,426
[b]	5	2,611	109,521
—	—	298	40,580
11	50	11	50
151,794	2,733,824	242,561	9,094,538
—	—	8,752	835,649
—	—	8,462	1,005,844
—	—	28	7,569
—	—	1	118
142,653	2,721,871	225,856	8,082,788
—	—	1	647
170	3,453	187	16,484
3,266	80,057	3,266	80,057
—	—	19	1,738
—	—	18	3,239
23	300	23	300
146,112	2,805,681	246,613	10,034,433

Mercury

Quicksilver is the descriptive term applied to this heavy white metal, liquid at ordinary temperature, which bears the name of the fleet-footed messenger of the gods. Elusive as that temperamental character, the element is seldom found undisguised. It usually occurs in the form of its sulfide known as cinnabar, a reddish mineral which in the pure state contains as much as 86.2 percent of mercury.

Although ores containing as little as 0.5 percent of the metal are actually utilized, they have far less economic value than those of higher grade, for all mercury ores must be reduced to the metallic condition to be used. In fact, many of the best-known applications of this element require the liquid form, and all its commercially important compounds are produced from metallic mercury.

Appearing on the market as a metal which, due to its weight, requires a substantial container, mercury is universally bought and used in a "flask" of wrought-iron, fitted with a screw plug and holding about 76 pounds.

Cinnabar is found in several countries, including our own, but the largest deposits are located in Spain and Italy and from the first of these come the highest grade ores. Back in 1645 the Spanish Government assumed the working of one of the largest and richest groups of mercury mines in the world—the Almaden mines in Ciudad Real, which still furnish about one-third of the total world production of mercury.

Italy, however, has even more extensive mercury mines in the Monte Amiata district, halfway between Rome and Florence. Reserves in these mines, all under the control of the Italian Government, are estimated to last twenty years at a production rate of 45,000 flasks annually.

The Mercurio Europeo, a cartel established in 1928, covers the combined output of Italy and Spain, and controls prices and quantities of sales from those countries.

The United States, now the third largest producer of mercury, at one time held the leading rank. The New Almaden mine in Santa Clara County, California, discovered in 1824 as a silver mine, proved about twenty years later to be exceedingly rich in cinnabar. That was just the time of the Gold Rush and the finding of a large source

MERCURY

WORLD PRODUCTION 1938

ITALY

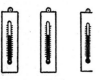

SPAIN

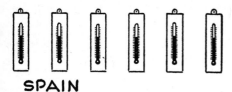

UNITED STATES

RUSSIA

MEXICO

EACH 🌡 REPRESENTS 225 METRIC TONS

of mercury was nothing short of providential, as this element was essential to extract the gold ores by amalgamation.

Other mines were later discovered in California, and in other states, but as they were worked more extensively the ores became less and less high-grade, and consequently the United States produced less and less mercury.

At present California, Oregon, Nevada, Arkansas and Arizona, in the order named, are the leading producing states, followed by Idaho, Texas and Washington. Few of the mines, owing to the low average tenor of the ore, can operate at a profit except at a high price for mercury; hence production fluctuated widely from year to year. It never exceeded 18,000 flasks, however, until 1939; and in 1940 twice that amount was produced—at a selling price of $176.87 per flask (40 percent above the peak figure for 1918).

Mexico has been producing small amounts of mercury for years, and there are many mines in that country. They are widely separated, however, and most of them are operated on a small scale by independent companies, with the result that Mexico produces normally only about 5,000 flasks of mercury a year.

Canada produced about 4,000 flasks of mercury in 1940 and will probably have an increasingly larger output, as intensive development has been carried on there. For instance, the Consolidated Mining and Smelting Company, which is exploiting cinnabar deposits at Ponchi Lake in British Columbia, is already able to ship about 400 flasks a month to Montreal for refining, although it has been operating only three years.

In general, the uses of mercury may be divided into two classes. In one it is completely consumed; in the other it acts only as an agent and remains unchanged in character.

The oldest use of this metal was for the recovery of gold and silver; but mercury is no longer absolutely indispensable for this purpose. For centuries a gold mine was of little value unless one of mercury was also available, and most of the cinnabar was discovered by men who had first found gold. Today, some hundred flasks of mercury are used in this way.

In the first category of its uses are its applications to the chemical field—in disinfectants and medicinals such as calomel, yellow oxide, mercurochrome, white precipitate, and so forth. These are responsible for the largest percentage of mercury consumption. It is important, too, in the manufacture of felt hats and amalgams for dental work.

Paramount among the uses in which the mercury remains unchanged are its applications to instruments (barometers, thermometers, and so forth) and in the electrical (storage batteries, rectifiers and switches) and mechanical fields.

The use of mercury as a generator of power is one of the newest and most interesting applications of this metal. W. L. N. Emmet, of the General Electric Company, is responsible for a process by which volatilized mercury is used to turn one turbine before being led into water where, as it condenses, it gives up its heat to convert the water into steam and turn a second turbine. Six and three-quarters pounds of mercury are required per kilowatt of energy; which means that about 300,000 pounds (4,000 flasks) are used but not consumed to produce a total of 45,000 kilowatts of energy. The element merely circulates—seven times an hour—and less than 1 percent is lost a year.

This process is now in operation at the General Electric plant at Schenectady and at public utility plants at Kearny, New Jersey, and Hartford, Connecticut. It seems logical to suppose that many more generators will one day be run on this economical system.

The strictly military uses of mercury are: in fulminates as a detonator for high explosives and in anti-fouling paints for naval vessels. Also important in time of war is the use of mercury in the manufacture of scientific and electrical instruments and its use in hospital disinfectants.

As for substitutes, it must be remembered that the particular properties which make mercury important—especially its liquid state at ordinary temperatures—are not found in any other metal; thus in many cases, such as in certain instruments, mercury cannot be replaced.

Lead azide and diazotinitrophenol have been used to some extent as a detonator, but they have not yet proved as reliable as mercury fulminate nor been standardized to a degree satisfactory for military use. As far as industrial disinfectants are concerned, other substances will suffice. Calomel is by no means indispensable. And the use of vermilion in paints and pigments is not essential.

In other words, the really military uses of this metal would merely intensify most of our demands in an emergency. Not one of them, fortunately, requires large amounts.

Consumption in 1940 has been estimated at 26,600 flasks or 11,177 less than domestic production and we were in a position to export the metal to countries cut off from their normal source of supply in Europe. The result was that by May shipments of domestic metal had increased to 2,300 flasks, which was far above our normal average monthly production.

This splurge in exports defeated the beneficial effects of our increased output and consumers began to draw on stocks to fill their requirements. Consequently, on July 2, 1940, the President signed a measure placing certain strategic materials, including mercury, under export control, and by August we were shipping no more mercury

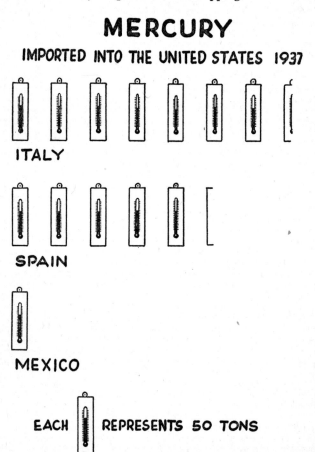

MERCURY

IMPORTED INTO THE UNITED STATES 1937

ITALY

SPAIN

MEXICO

EACH REPRESENTS 50 TONS

to such countries as Japan (to which we had sent 1,265 flasks in May and June). To the United Kingdom, however, shipments were increased from 2,507 flasks in the first half of the year, to 2,671 flasks in the latter half.

During the first few months of 1941, large Navy purchases of mercuric oxide for anti-fouling paint sent monthly consumption figures soaring, but once these had been filled a fairly normal rate was established. Yet as our "two ocean" navy becomes more and more a reality and as more A.E.F.'s spring up throughout the world the demand for anti-fouling paints will likely expand, helping to speed the day when sanity and security will once again prevail. It is fervently to be hoped that mercury (the fleet-footed messenger of the gods) will play an important role in that achievement.

The importance of mercury in the war program received full recognition in Conservation Order M-78, announced January 28, 1942, designed to conserve the supply of mercury for war purposes. The order provided that after February 15 no person shall use mercury in the manufacture of any item or process on List "A" of the order in excess of 50 percent of his requirements during a given base period, and that after March 31 he will entirely stop using mercury for such purposes.

Salient Statistics of the Mercury Industry in the United States, 1936-40

(FLASKS OF 76 POUNDS)

		1936	1937	1938	1939	1940
Production	flasks	16,569	16,508	17,991	18,633	37,777
Number of producing mines		87	101	91	107	159
Average price per flask:						
New York		$79.92	$90.18	$75.47	$103.94	$176.87
London		$64.33	$69.65	$66.92	$88.26	$201.10
Imports for consumption:						
Pounds		1,374,652	1,437,712	179,522	265,944	12,971
Equivalent flasks		18,088	18,917	2,362	3,499	171
Exports:						
Pounds		19,980	34,485	54,161	91,789	730,877
Equivalent flasks		263	454	713	1,208	9,617
Apparent new supply	flasks	34,400	35,000	19,600	20,900	26,600[a]
From domestic mines	percent	47	46	88	83	100
Stocks in warehouses (bonded) at end of year	flasks	2,513	4,286	553	3,110	901

[a] Actual consumption as reported by consumers.

Antimony

Of all the strategic metals none has more uses of a direct military character than antimony, and only mercury has applications of possibly greater military importance. Both metals are employed in the making of ammunition, and just which is more necessary in time of war would be a rhetorical question, since the shrapnel balls and bullets requiring antimony could not be fired without the mercury fulminate to send them off and the latter would have no significance without the bullets and shrapnel it is used to detonate.

Curiously enough, both of these essential materials are used in very small amounts. Not more than 12 percent of antimony is required in the lead alloys it is used to harden (and this is the way most antimony is consumed) and sometimes only 4 percent is necessary. Consequently, total world consumption of antimony is usually only about 25,000 tons a year and the peak demand in the last war was not much more than 60,000 tons.

Antimonial lead is produced either by alloying the two metals or, as is more often the case, by the smelting of antimonial lead ores or a mixture of lead ores and antimony. The chief ore of this silvery-white metal—and the only one of any commercial importance—is stibnite, the trisulfide, of which there are large deposits in China and Bolivia, less important ones in Mexico, and small and scattered mines in several other countries, including our own.

Lead hardened by alloying with various proportions of antimony ore is used for many other things besides bullets and shrapnel. Babbitt and other friction-bearing metals account for about 32 percent of our consumption; battery-plates, type-metal about 22 percent; soft metal alloys and solder 12 percent; hard lead for pipes and traps 10 percent; and vulcanized rubber and rubber goods 7 percent. Other important uses include cable coverings and the enamel on metal ware; while antimony compounds are used for medicinal purposes; in the white smoke employed for range finding; in dyes, paints, pigments and fire preventives; and in the handling of certain extremely important chemicals—such as sulfuric acid, the *sine qua non* not only of industry in general but of munitions factories in particular.

Here, then, we have a material of which we use comparatively small quantities—12,000 to 18,000 tons a year in normal times, probably not more than 20,000 tons in time of war—but which we must have if we are to maintain our production of industrial metals and manufacture certain weapons of defense.

We import, at the present time, about half of the antimony we consume—principally from Mexico and Bolivia. There are deposits in Nevada, Colorado, Alaska and Idaho where developments are being carried on, but these could not be worked with profit unless the price of antimony were increased to three times the usual 10 cents a pound. And even then we probably could not produce more than 17,000 tons a year—after three years of higher prices.

What we could count on, however, is our domestic production of by-product and "secondary recovery" antimony. Our highly developed lead smelting industry provides a considerable amount of antimonial lead, which yielded 2,077 tons of antimony in 1940, of which 1,915 tons came from domestic ores.

Also from domestic ores—this time gold and silver deposits—is the antimony recovered in the Yellow Pine District of Idaho, where the antimony content is estimated to be about 2 or 3 percent. This means that from the installed plant capacity of 60,000 short tons of ore we can count on 900 tons of recoverable metal.

This would help in an emergency but we would depend still more on the secondary recovery of antimony from old alloys, scrap and dross—the source now of about 35 percent of our annual domestic consumption. The total production of antimony from secondary metals in 1940 equaled 11,421 tons, 16 percent more than in 1939; most of it came from old scrap which consisted principally of discarded storage batteries. And in a pinch the tonnage of secondary antimony scrap could be considerably increased.

Moreover, many of our present industrial uses of antimony could be dispensed with. In cable lead, calcium can be substituted for antimony; and in the manufacture of rubber goods, enamel ware, chemicals and paints, for instance, we might be able to use other metals, thus saving about 10,000 short tons of antimony. Also, by reducing its use in making babbitt and other bearing metals, cable coverings and various other materials, a saving of at least 9,000 short tons could be effected.

But even more important is the fact that a new metal has been developed which has been officially accepted by the Ordnance Department as a substitute for antimonial lead in the making of shrapnel and bullets. Thanks to this material, called Frary metal, we can

ANTIMONY

WORLD PRODUCTION 1937

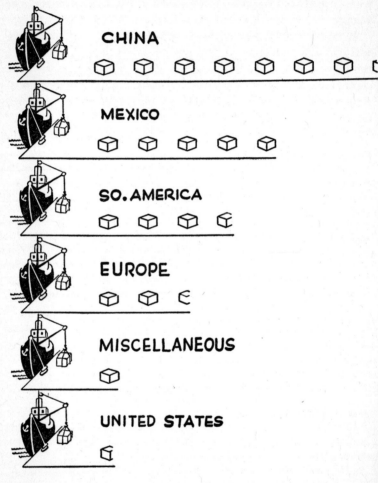

probably, if absolutely necessary, make our domestic sources of antimony suffice. But it is unlikely that we shall not be able to avail ourselves of the output of the Mexican mines. There are also deposits in
Argentina, Chile, Bolivia and Canada, though none of these has been
exploited to the extent that the Mexican ores have been mined.

When the last world war began we were dependent upon China, which is still the source of more than half of the world's supply of antimony. We were forced at that time to look around for other sources of this metal and it was then that most of our own deposits were investigated and those in Mexico and Bolivia intensively developed.

In Bolivia, which exported the metal to England, the antimony was obtained from numerous small deposits worked by Indians in the most primitive and wasteful manner, so that when war prices came to an end the mining could not be continued and the Indians returned to their former occupations (or lack of them) and the mines were left deserted—waiting for another war boom!

The Mexican mines, too, were forced to shut down for a while, but were later reopened and have continued to function with increasing efficiency. Since 1930 most of the mineral used in this country has come from Mexico and been smelted at Laredo, Texas.

Therefore, unless by some evil chance Mexico falls into the hands of a hostile power, we can depend upon our usual source of supply of antimony.

Antimony Imported into the United States in 1939, by Countries

(SHORT TONS)

COUNTRY	ORE ANTIMONY CONTENT	METAL
Belgium	—	191
Mexico	6,346	125
China	—	661
Great Britain	—	12
Argentina[a]	218	—
Bolivia	2,454	—
Peru	430	—
France	—	56

[a] Imports credited to Argentina originate largely in Bolivia.

Salient Statistics for Antimony in the
United States, 1936-40

		1936	1937	1938	1939	1940
Production of antimony ore and concentrates	Short tons	3,867	4,250	2,730	3,174	1,124
Antimony contained	do	755	1,266	650	393	494
Antimony content of antimonial lead produced from domestic and foreign ores	Short tons	1,471	1,726	2,080	1,108	2,077
Secondary antimony produced	do	9,900	12,340	8,500	9,810	11,421
Imports for consumption:						
Antimony in ore	do	10,545	13,818	8,322	9,448	15,733
Needle or liquated antimony	do	1,185	772	90	228	113
Metal	do	1,171	1,043	821	1,045	209
Oxide	do	1,201	1,118	414	167	—
Exports of foreign antimony	do	392	437	711	58	276
Primary antimony available for consumption	do	15,040	18,132	11,557	11,609	17,955
Stocks of antimony in bonded warehouse at end of year	do	443	656	345	685	3,417
Average price of antimony at New York:[a]						
Chinese	Cents per pound	12.97	15.30	14.59	14.44	16.50
American	do	12.25	15.35	12.35	12.36	14.00
World production	Short tons	38,900	42,100	35,600	[b]	[b]

[a] According to American Metal Market.
[b] Figures not yet available.

Mica

Mica is one of the few strategic minerals that is used alone rather than in alloys or other compounds; in fact, the form in which it is most familiar to us all is in the finely ground particles that sparkle as "snow" on our Christmas trees.

We must make it clear from the outset, however, that mica is not an element but a generic term applied to a whole group of non-metallic minerals, all highly complex silicates of aluminum and one or more other bases. The two most important are the potash mica, called muscovite or white mica, and phlogopite, the amber mica with a magnesium base.

The characteristic which distinguishes these minerals from all others is their property of crystallizing with such profound cleavage planes that they may be split up into thin sheets. The sheets are transparent, flexible, tough, highly resistant to temperature, atmospheric and chemical corrosion, and are non-conductors of heat and electricity.

Obviously, mica sheets are extremely useful to the electrical industry, especially as they may be cut or split according to specified dimensions. Flat discs or washers can be made for electrical appliances of various sizes and shapes; flexible forms may be fashioned on which to wind the heating elements of toasters, irons, heat-pads and so forth; plates of divers sizes can be cut to place between the segments of the commutators of dynamos and generators both large and small, or between the leaves of the electric condensers of radios or the engines of planes and cars.

War demands greatly increase all the electrical uses of mica, and many military requirements of the mineral are identical with civilian needs, such as radio sending and receiving sets, airplane spark plugs, motors and generators. In all these uses the mica must be extremely pure. The presence of other minerals that are conductors of electricity would be fatal, as would a faulty mica sheet that wore out before the copper segments it was used to separate.

For most of these strategically important applications high-grade mica alone will do. No other substance has been proved to possess such high dielectric strength under high temperatures. A synthetic product has been developed, it is true, consisting of tough, flexible bentonite films, and this is reported to have an electric resistance comparable with mica's, but it is too new for any one to know to just what extent it might reduce the demand for mica.

That is why this mineral is on the strategic list. We must have high-grade mica for the electrical industry, radios, planes and cars in wartime, and this country does not produce more than 26 percent of the high-grade sheet mica necessary to meet our normal needs, much less our emergency requirements.

We have an ample supply of low-grade mica ore—suitable for ground mica, which is used in large quantities for tires, rubber products, paints, roofing materials, wallpaper, and plastics, as well as for isinglass, which has its military uses—in gas masks and eye-protectors where transparency must be combined with resistance to heat and shock.

Our largest deposits of mica occur in North Carolina and New Hampshire, where we now produce annually about 40,000,000 pounds of ground mica but only a little over 1,000,000 pounds of sheet mica. Additional reserves are to be found in several other states, but none of them contain high-grade ore which could be made, economically, into the "sheets" or "splittings" of which we use about 4,000,000 pounds a year.

Most of this mica we import from India, the rest from Canada. These two countries, with Madagascar, are the principal producers of sheets and splittings, though there are deposits of fairly high-grade mica in several other countries, including Argentina and Brazil. Canada and Madagascar are the only producers of amber mica.

The Canadian output of splittings is capable of considerable expansion at a higher price, and splittings are our real problem, since the production of sheet mica in this country could be increased to provide for our war needs if necessary. We produced over 2,000,000 pounds in 1926, under the stimulus of high prices, and we could certainly do it again.

With splittings alone, then, let us see what our situation would be in case we could not import for war needs. We usually have one year's supply on hand, in addition to two or three months' supply of manufactured goods, and at a high enough price for mica we could probably produce the amount of splittings necessary to fulfil our most urgent needs. Mica-splitting machines, such as have recently been developed, could triple the rate and greatly reduce the cost of output, and at the end of two years we could be producing probably at a rate of 4,000,000 pounds of splittings a year.

Meanwhile, we could be getting Canadian splittings and some black mica from Brazil, Argentina, Guatemala and Bolivia, so our condition need never be really serious where mica is concerned. It would entail some effort and expense to put our industry on a war basis, but it could be done.

MICA
WORLD PRODUCTION 1939

UNITED STATES

INDIA - BRITISH

EACH ⬡ REPRESENTS 4,000 METRIC TONS

Salient Statistics of the Mica Industry
in the United States, 1936-40

	1936	1937	1938	1939	1940
Domestic mica sold or used by producers:					
Total uncut sheet and punch:					
Pounds	1,319,233	1,694,538	939,507	813,708	1,625,437
Value	$203,879	$285,244	$139,333	$138,963	$291,685
Average per pound	$0.15	$0.17	$0.15	$0.17	$0.18
Scrap:[a]					
Short tons	20,955	25,196	20,257	24,672	22,386
Value	$260,594	$354,737	$256,382	$311,895	$314,565
Average per ton	$12.44	$14.08	$12.66	$12.64	$14.05
Total sheet and scrap:[a]					
Short tons	21,615	26,043	20,727	25,079	23,199
Value	$464,473	$639,981	$395,715	$450,858	$606,250
Total ground:[a]					
Short tons	25,585	27,245	27,086	30,924	27,984
Value	$722,416	$839,812	$924,554	$1,156,333	$1,016,628
Consumption of splittings:[b]					
Pounds	3,518,058	4,347,435	1,667,806	3,423,044	4,918,861
Value	$846,393	$1,257,645	$612,465	$1,089,683	$1,725,522
Imports for consumption:					
Total uncut sheet and punch:					
Pounds	860,253	1,004,950	391,125	902,598	1,534,188
Value	$239,378	$296,235	$113,403	$271,072	$576,565
Scrap:					
Short tons	3,893	6,723	4,450	4,279	3,061
Value	$22,666	$36,355	$28,590	$29,493	$22,611
Total sheet and scrap:					
Short tons	4,323	7,226	4,646	4,730	3,828
Value	$262,044	$332,590	$141,993	$300,565	$599,176
Manufactured:					
Short tons	2,355	4,113	1,115	1,550	3,860
Value	$943,524	$1,735,009	$522,426	$758,745	$1,884,952
Total imports:					
Short tons	6,678	11,339	5,761	6,280	7,688
Value	$1,205,568	$2,067,599	$664,419	$1,059,310	$2,484,128
Exports (all classes of mica):					
Short tons	1,478	1,795	1,772	1,827	903
Value	$170,011	$216,858	$183,889	$226,364	$191,550

[a] Includes mica recovered from kaolin and mica schists, as follows: 1936, 8,258 tons, $127,343; 1937, 10,536 tons, $149,931; 1938, 6,550 tons, $86,602; 1939, 10,011 tons, $108,899; 1940, 9,674 tons, $138,148.

[b] Exclusive of a nominal quantity of splittings produced in the United States and South America.

Consumption and Stocks of Mica Splittings in the United States, 1936-40, by Sources, as Reported by the Consumers

	INDIA		CANADA	
	Pounds	*Value*	*Pounds*	*Value*
Consumption:[a]				
1936	3,051,824	$649,982	102,766	$44,566
1937	3,721,594	965,418	98,618	51,960
1938	1,446,349	511,674	41,100	20,401
1939	2,995,626	905,763	107,101	44,065
1940	4,252,120	1,358,534	54,044	28,491
Stocks in consumers' hands Dec. 31:				
1936	1,280,517	304,036	52,014	19,048
1937	3,920,730	1,094,414	77,130	33,722
1938	4,057,681	1,128,075	55,827	24,378
1939	2,754,748	857,656	52,523	17,697
1940	4,620,934	1,776,974	53,378	35,581

	MADAGASCAR		TOTAL	
	Pounds	*Value*	*Pounds*	*Value*
Consumption:[a]				
1936	363,468	$151,845	3,518,058	$846,393
1937	527,223	240,267	4,347,435	1,257,645
1938	180,357	80,390	1,667,806	612,465
1939	320,317	139,855	3,423,044	1,089,683
1940	612,697	338,497	4,918,861	1,725,522
Stocks in consumers' hands Dec. 31:				
1936	233,357	101,711	1,555,888	424,795
1937	444,762	195,976	4,442,622	1,324,112
1938	631,119	273,926	4,744,627	1,426,379
1939	673,354	273,465	3,480,625	1,148,818
1940	738,489	410,068	5,412,801	2,222,623

[a] Exclusive of a nominal quantity of splittings produced in the United States and South America.

Quartz Crystal

Silicon dioxide (quartz), commonly known as rock crystal, is one of the most abundant and widely distributed minerals, and is found in a variety of forms. The one which is important for our purposes is a particular species of crystal called "Brazilian pebble" because that country has long been the only commercial source of quartz, which has a certain purity and size.

The particular characteristic of "Brazilian pebbles" which makes them strategically significant is their piezoelectrical property—the faculty of generating an electrical potential when placed under stress. In other words, when a plate cut from a crystal in a certain direction is placed under tension or pressure, an electric charge of measurable proportions is developed on that plate; while, on the other hand, if an electrical charge is applied to the same plate in a particular manner, there is an immediate change in its dimensions.

It is because of this property that quartz-plate oscillators are used in radio transmitters and receivers, in controlling the frequency of general radio transmission, in establishing frequency standards, and in television and precise wireless telephony; while radio (quartz) crystals in airplane guidance and communication permit immediate reception not obtainable by any other means.

Quartz-plate resonators are also used at the terminals of oceanic cables and in local and long-distance telephone lines, where they make it possible to divide the range of frequencies into bands—which means that hundreds of independent messages may be transmitted over a single wire at one time.

For depth-sounding and iceberg detection apparatus, quartz crystal is invaluable, as the quartz plates in these instruments can be made to vibrate at high frequencies, generating directional waves which are reflected from the sea bottom or from an obstruction at sea. By measuring the time interval between the emission and return of these waves the depth of the sea or the distance from the obstruction (iceberg) may be determined.

Similarly, quartz crystal is employed in sound detecting and locating devices for use against submarines and airplanes. And another strategic use is in range-finding instruments and in measuring the pressure developed by a propellant charge in a gun barrel, making possible the prediction of the distance a given projectile will travel when propelled by a given charge.

A number of precision instruments—such as clocks which must be super-accurate, direct-reading seismographs, periscopes, gun sights, radio phonograph pick-ups, and polariscopes—require quartz crystal in their construction; and it is extensively used in the manufacture of special water-clear lenses and prisms, submarine windows, laboratory vessels and for the transmission of light where the passage of the ultraviolet ray is desirable.

We must not fail to mention the application of quartz crystal to the jewelry trade, as it is employed to a very large extent in the manufacture of inexpensive jewelry. Ground into grains and powder, it is valuable as a cutting and polishing material in the manufacture of glass and porcelain. For both of these uses crystals with defects will do.

In the case of radio frequency and for precision instruments only high-grade "Brazilian pebble" will suffice. Crystals for these purposes must be optically clear and should have growth lines on the faces. The part employed in making frequency control crystals must be "free from flaws, cracks, ghosts, phantoms, veils, needles, bubbles, twinning." They may be square, round, rectangular, in various sizes and thicknesses. The size most frequently employed is one inch square. The cutting of these crystals is done by means of iron wheels used with carborundum or diamond saws. They are brought to dimension by lapping on flat iron wheels, again using abrasives.

We can best understand the degree of precision required in the making of these tiny oscillating plates when we consider the allowable variation in physical thickness, which is only six ten-millionths of an inch in commercial frequency limits. Crystals cut with this accuracy can be designed to operate at definite frequencies ranging from about 20,000 to 20,000,000 per second.

It is not only the cutting of these crystals which requires great technical skill; making holders for them is a very ticklish job, for the holder must permit free vibration of the crystal and at the same time afford adequate protection against dirt and moisture. One touch of a small drop of water may cause a crystal to cease vibrating. In crystals for use in planes moisture protection is particularly important because of the condensation and freezing of moisture when an airplane climbs from a low altitude and warm temperature to a freezing level, and the ice film which melts when the plane drops from the freezing to the warm air.

There are about forty other materials known to have piezoelectrical property, but they all have certain other characteristics which make them unsuitable for radio frequency control. Not even inferior grades of quartz crystal will do. Only about one-fourth the total weight of Brazilian exports (1,494,000 pounds in 1939), which represent approximately the entire world output, can be put to this strategic use.

Deposits of the high-grade crystals in Brazil appear, however, to be extensive, sufficient to meet world requirements for many years. Procuring the quartz is not simple, however. Mining is done mostly by pick and shovel from small open workings, and the mines located in the States of Minas Geraes, Bahia, and Goyas are unorganized and at great distances from shipping centers. Some of the high-grade crystals must be transported 1,100 miles by mule-back before they reach a railroad about 700 miles from Rio de Janeiro.

Up until late 1941 Japan was the most important market for Brazilian quartz, taking about 60 percent of the total exports in terms of quantity, 44 percent in terms of value. This difference was due to the fact that most of the Japanese purchases consisted of small, low-grade crystals used in cheap jewelry, and of some optical quartz.

Purchases for the United States, on the other hand, which normally represented only 4.6 percent of the total quantity of quartz exported from Brazil, accounted for nearly 15 percent of the total value of that quartz because buyers in this country needed the high-grade crystals with piezoelectrical properties.

Our Government has initiated stock-pile buying in Brazil, taking practically the entire output without regard to size or quality; hence exports from there during the last four months have exceeded the total exports of the previous two years.

Quartz Crystal (Rock Crystal): Exports (Domestic Produce) from
Brazil to Principal Markets, in Specified Years, 1929 to 1939

(IN 1,000 POUNDS)

COUNTRY	1929	1932	1936	1937	1938	1939
Total, all countries	1,099	680	495	661	1,647	1,494
Japan	584	588	337	451	965	843
United Kingdom	9	5	28	88	361	360
Germany	246	36	51	66	212	203
United States	44	19	27	38	72	62
Netherlands	198	13	17	2	17	17
Italy	1	—	—	1	9	1
China	17	15	2	12	8	3
All other	—	4	33	3	3	4
Percentage to the United States	4.0	2.7	5.5	5.8	4.4	4.1

SOURCE: Consular report Quartz Crystal in Brazil, June 24, 1939, and report of Brazilian
Ministry of Finance, 1939.

Platinum

Platinum (now largely a symbol of presupposed wedded bliss) formed part of the loot of the *Conquistadores* of the sixteenth century, who found it in Colombia associated with placer gold. They named the silvery metal "platina" and brought it back to Spain more as a curiosity than anything else.

And curiosity it remained until nineteenth century chemists discovered that its resistance to chemical attack and oxidation and its high melting-point, made it the ideal material for crucibles and other laboratory equipment, and that it was a suitable catalyst for making concentrated sulfuric acid.

By the end of the last century numerous industrial uses had been found for platinum—principally in the electrical field—and its value in dental work had been established.

And, finally, about forty years ago, jewelers conceived the idea of using platinum as a setting for precious stones; they made this metal more fashionable than gold, and consequently brought about a tremendous increase in the price of platinum. Formerly about the same price as gold, it became seven or eight times as expensive during the First World War. And more and more if it was used to make jewelry.

This decisive change in the fortunes of platinum has had three far-reaching and, for us, very happy results.

First, the increase in the price of platinum led to the search for new sources of supply, and this in turn brought about the development of deposits not only in far-off South Africa but also in Colombia, Canada and Alaska. And these mines can now be counted on to furnish us with platinum for our war needs. During the last World War we were dependent upon Russia, which used to supply over 90 percent of the world's total output. Today the rich Sudbury mines of Canada yield over one-half of all the platinum used in the world; the remaining half is produced by Russia, South Africa, Colombia and the United States.

The second fortunate result of platinum's increase in prestige and price was the effort of its industrial and chemical consumers to find substitutes for this metal (the strategic significance of which will be discussed later), and the third was the tremendous reserve supply of the metal built up in this country by the manufacturers and accumulators of platinum jewelry.

In jewelry platinum, hardened with a small amount of iridium or ruthenium, is used. These are two of the several sister metals recoverable from the platinum ore; the others are: rhodium, palladium and osmium, of which palladium is by far the most important.

Useful for medium-duty electrical contacts, palladium is also alloyed with gold to produce "white gold," which, though about the same price as gold, is only about half as expensive to use because of its low specific gravity. This makes it desirable for dental work and it is used for dental purposes all over the world, but not as frequently as palladium in its pure state.

Rhodium is never used alone; but combined with platinum (in the proportion of 90 percent platinum to 10 percent rhodium) it makes a material for wire which, joined to pure platinum wires, forms thermocouples that furnish an accurate way of measuring high temperatures. Above all, rhodium-platinum catalyst is used for the production of nitrate from the air.

Osmium, the heaviest metal known, always occurs associated with iridium, and this natural alloy has been used for the tips of gold pens, while iridium alloyed with platinum is employed in making various types of electrical equipment. Ruthenium has largely replaced iridium in hardening platinum for jewelry purposes.

As a matter of fact, the total output and consumption of all the platinum by-metals, though becoming increasingly important, is still small.

Platinum itself is not used in large amounts. Take 1929, for instance, when we reached the peak of our output of internal combustion engines and electrical equipment and when industry in general was booming and the consumption of nitric and sulfuric acids was also at its height. That year we consumed only 191,619 ounces of all the platinum metals.

In 1940 we used 206,890 ounces, of which platinum itself accounted for over 59 percent. About 42 percent of the platinum (51,296 ounces) went to the jewelry trade, 25 percent (31,174 ounces) to the electrical industry, and only 8 percent (9,859 ounces) to the dental industry.

Of the total 206,890 ounces of platinum metals sold to consumers in this country in 1940, 195,645 ounces were imported—35,659 ounces from Canada and 34,011 ounces from Colombia.

Since both of these countries produced much more platinum than was sold to us that year our imports from these two neighbors could be greatly increased. This means that though stocks on hand on December 31, 1940, were only 269,914 ounces, or not very much more than the year's consumption, our situation with regard to platinum was very good—even if substitutes for platinum did not exist.

And as a matter of fact, there are substitutes to replace platinum in practically all of its industrial uses. If we leave out the alloys of nickel and chromium, which might, in themselves, present problems of procurement, those of palladium and silver could be used to resist spark erosion in ignition apparatus; platenite (an iron-nickel alloy coated with copper) is already replacing platinum in connecting wire in incandescent lamps; tungsten has taken its place in ignition devices, magnetos and sparking points; and various other alloys are now used for resistance wirings in electric furnaces and for thermocouples.

As for the chemical industry, vanadium catalysts are being used to an ever-increasing extent, particularly in the making of sulfuric acid; and where vanadium is not used, a platinized silicogel, which reduces the consumption of platinum about 81 percent, is often adopted.

Even in laboratory equipment other metals, such as tantalum, nickel, tungsten and nickel, chromium and rustless iron alloys, besides certain non-metallic substances, including fused quartz, porcelain, and artificial corundum, have been used to replace platinum. While certain of these, like nickel, tungsten and chromium, might not be plentiful during a long war, we could probably manage to make crucibles somehow out of materials on hand.

There seems, therefore, to be no reason why platinum should ever present a serious procurement problem. As one authority has expressed it, its presence on the strategic list may be merely a "hangover" from the last war.

PLATINUM -
ALLIED METALS

WORLD PRODUCTION 1939

CANADA

RUSSIA

UNION OF SO. AFRICA

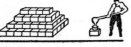

UNITED STATES

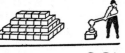

COLOMBIA

EACH REPRESENTS 50,000 TROY OUNCES

Platinum Metals (Unmanufactured) Imported for Consumption in the United States in 1940, by Countries, in Troy Ounces

COUNTRY	PLATINUM Ores of platinum metals (platinum content)	Grain and nuggets	Sponge and Scrap	Ingots, bars, sheets, or plates not less than ⅛-in. thick	IRIDIUM	OSMIUM AND OSMIRIDIUM	PALLADIUM	RHODIUM AND RUTHENIUM	TOTAL
Argentina	—	284	128	—	—	—	5	—	417
Australia	—	—	558	—	—	45	—	—	603
Brazil	—	11	7	—	—	—	—	—	18
Canada	12,177	10,168	880	—	—	—	10,168	2,266	35,659
China	—	294	—	—	—	—	—	—	294
Colombia	1,004	28,266	4,741	—	—	—	—	—	34,011
Cuba	—	—	—	108	—	—	—	—	108
El Salvador	—	—	—	10	—	—	—	—	10
France	—	—	—	146	—	—	—	—	146
Japan	—	—	142	—	—	—	—	9	151
Norway	311	342	—	—	—	—	443	—	1,096
Panama	155	—	—	—	—	—	—	—	155
Switzerland	—	—	20	—	—	—	—	—	20
United Kingdom	6	5,302	26,258	35,378	237	3,474	49,588	2,759	122,957
	13,653	44,667	32,734	35,642	237	3,474	60,204	5,034	195,645

World Production of Platinum and Allied Metals, 1936-40, in Troy Ounces

(Compiled by L. P. Lounsbery)

	1936	1937	1938	1939	1940
Australia:					
New South Wales: Placer platinum	47	46	8	a	a
Tasmania: Placer osmiridium	281	586	191	283	a
Belgian Congo: From refineries:					
Palladium	12,571	12,507	1,575	a	a
Platinum	3,183	2,122	225	a	a
Canada:					
Placer platinum	20	22	16	25	a
From refineries:[b]					
Platinum	131,551	139,355	161,310	148,877	a
Other platinum metals	103,671	119,829	130,893	135,402	a

World Production of Platinum and Allied Metals, 1936-40, in Troy Ounces (*continued*)

(*Compiled by L. P. Lounsbery*)

	1936	1937	1938	1939	1940
Colombia:					
Placer platinum (exports)	38,333	29,315	34,549	39,070	a
Ethiopia: Placer platinum	8,038	a	a	a	a
Italy: From refineries:					
Platinum	836	1,286	1,029	a	a
Japan: Placer platinum	34	a	a	a	a
Netherlands Indies (probably placer platinum)	—	—	21	28	a
New Zealand: Placer platinum	29	55	1	13	a
Panama: Placer platinum	19	267	—	—	—
Papua: c					
Placer platinum	21	20	41	2	a
Placer osmiridium	17	8	4	4	a
Sierra Leone: Placer platinum	484	308	180	83	a
Union of South Africa:					
Platinum (content of platinum metals) d	19,751	17,776	18,256	18,068	a
Concentrates (content of platinum metals) d	13,163	21,849	35,124	41,243	a
Osmiridium e	5,431	5,790	5,354	7,031	a
U.S.S.R.: Placer platinum f	100,000	100,000	100,000	100,000	100,000
United States:					
Placer platinum	9,875	10,803	40,932	32,460	36,500 g
Ore (content of platinum metals)	110	124	90	66	—
From refineries: h					
Platinum	4,443	4,761	3,761	5,270	4,470
Other platinum metals	4,541	5,817	3,486	3,364	3,304
	456,000	473,000 i	537,000 i	531,000 j	a

a Data not available.

b Recovered from nickel-copper mattes.

c Year ended June 30 of year stated.

d Produced from platinum ores.

e Produced from treatment of gold ores on the Rand.

f Estimated production.

g Subject to revision.

h New platinum metals recovered in gold and copper refining of domestic materials.

i Exclusive of Ethiopia and Japan.

j Exclusive of New South Wales, Belgian Congo, Ethiopia, Italy, and Japan.

Salient Statistics of Platinum and Allied Metals in the United States, 1939-40, in Troy Ounces

	1939	*1940*
Production:		
Crude platinum from placers	32,460	36,500[a]
New metals:		
Platinum	36,033[b]	38,951[b]
Palladium	3,491	4,564
Other	1,917	3,824
	41,441	47,339
Secondary metals:		
Platinum	45,432	47,657
Palladium	13,039	14,773
Other	4,972	4,000
	63,443	66,430
Stocks in hands of refiners, Dec. 31:[c]		
Platinum	71,393	144,302[c]
Palladium	29,273	93,244[c]
Other	16,884	32,368[c]
	117,550	269,914[c]
Imports for consumption:		
Platinum	190,226	126,696
Palladium	96,829	60,204
Other	19,572	8,745
	306,627	195,645
Exports:		
Unmanufactured	46,329	55,027
Manufactures (except jewelry)	4,041	1,800

[a] Subject to revision.

[b] In 1940 includes 8,427 ounces (8,205 in 1939) of new platinum from domestic sources, comprising 3,957 ounces (2,919 in 1939) derived from crude placer platinum, none (16 ounces in 1939) from ore, and 4,470 ounces (5,270 in 1939) obtained from domestic gold and copper ores as a by-product of refining.

[c] Beginning with 1940, figures include stocks held in the United States by importers of platinum-group metals from the United Kingdom.

Optical Glass

Before the last World War Germany had a virtual monopoly on optical glass and this country produced very few of the instruments requiring precision lenses—instruments vitally needed in modern warfare.

At the time of the Civil War artillery was fired at point-blank ranges; the enemy was visible and distance could be estimated by the naked eye. With the increase in both power and precision of modern guns, however, it became possible to attack targets at greater and greater distances. Moreover, firing was now directed at objects either below the horizon or hidden by intervening obstacles. Consequently, fire control became an engineering problem requiring precise instruments, upon the quality of which depended the effectiveness of both military and naval artillery.

No wonder, then, that in 1917, when we were faced with war and had almost no stocks of optical glass and no means of replenishment from abroad, the Government looked about for someone to teach the people of this country to make their own.

Dr. Arthur L. Day, director of the Geophysical Laboratory of the Carnegie Institute, who had been studying silicate solutions similar to optical glass, began an immediate survey of the country's facilities, and Dr. F. E. Wright was put at the head of a group of scientists assigned to the Bausch and Lomb plant in April of that year.

The Government required 2,000 pounds of optical glass a day, but that amount a month was about all that could be expected from the one producing plant and from those still in the experimental stage. We had all the raw materials: oxides of lead, zinc and silica, nitrates or carbonates. What we did not have in such abundance were skilled glass-workers used to the long and tedious process required to produce fine lenses.

Many hours of carefully watched heating; weeks of gradual cooling, during which the glass must be minutely examined; a very exact re-heating to form the lens; and then the crucial "annealing" or cooling-off before the scrupulous final inspection—these are the stages necessary to produce optical glass, and each one requires expert workmanship.

During the short time we were at war we managed to train the men for this and to produce the glass—enough by June, 1918, to meet our essential military and naval needs.

However, after the world was supposedly "back to normalcy" this newly formed industry found it difficult to meet foreign competition, due to the cheapness of skilled labor abroad; and without a 50 percent tariff on "blanks" and an even higher tax on imported finished products, it is doubtful whether we would have been able to supply even half of our domestic peacetime needs.

This we have been doing, fortunately; and we now have at our disposal a number of plants which could be expanded if necessary, as well as skilled workmen to train more men. Also, we have been acquiring war reserves sufficient to supply our needs while domestic production was being speeded up.

During the war emergency our position with regard to optical glass will probably be more than tenable—though careful planning will be necessary for economical and effective use.

Phenol

The "plastic age" in which we are living owes its beginning to phenol—that is, to the synthetic variety of this substance. For it was the superabundance of the latter, left over after the last war, which caused American chemists to undertake the commercial research which led to the large-scale development of the synthetic resin industry.

The reason we had so much synthetic phenol on hand was because, lacking sufficient of the natural product to make enough of the high explosive, picric acid, we had built large plants to produce phenol from benzine, of which we had plenty.

Germany had a practical monopoly on all the coal-tar products at that time, and phenol was only one of several which we needed badly and learned to make during the last war. Some of the others—such as dye-stuffs—had a large peacetime market, but synthetic phenol did not; and by the end of 1918 the United States Government had over 35,000,000 pounds of this synthetic product on hand.

It was finally put to very good use (though the expensive plants which had produced it were shut down) by the ingenuity of the chemists who developed the phenolic resins, such as bakelite, which formed the basis of the ever-increasing plastics industry.

War babies of 1918, plastics are playing an important role in the present conflict. Planes and tanks, guns and gas masks, all have some plastic parts and many of them are formulated in part of phenol.

In this war, picric acid has not been in great demand, since the French, who use picrates in their explosives, are *hors de combat*. However, Russia does use large quantities.

There are other applications of phenol which have strategic importance, such as its use as an antiseptic (it is sometimes called crystal carbolic acid) and in the manufacture of aspirin—acetysalicylic acid, produced from salicylic acid, which in turn is the product of phenol and an alkali treated with carbon dioxide.

Civilian uses include preservatives, solvents and dyes. In fact, picric acid was used as a yellow pigment long before its destructive qualities were discovered. But it is really the ever-increasing vogue for synthetic plastics that has created the greatest market for phenol.

Thanks to our love for shiny gadgets, our annual production of phenol (about 1,000,000 pounds in 1914) is now about 65,000,000 pounds, which means that we are already equipped to make a large percentage of our civilian needs; and by expanding present plant capacity we will soon be able to furnish sufficient phenol for all military and naval requirements.

The latest development is a new process so efficient that it is said to yield less than one-tenth of a pound of by-products per pound of phenol. Developed by Durez Plastics and Chemicals, Incorporated, this process is now being used in their new plant at North Tonawanda, New York, where phenol is being produced at an annual rate of over 15,000,000 pounds. Since this capacity could be greatly increased the Durez plant among others offers us assurance of sufficient supplies of phenol for essential uses. While exact information is lacking, it is quite certain that all of the principal producers of phenol in this country—Barrett, Dow, Monsanto and others—have already increased productive capacity or are rapidly doing so.

In other words, instead of the natural product's being supplemented by the synthetic, it may turn out to be just the reverse, as most of our present production of phenol is from benzene. With a large and vigorous organic chemical industry, we can now produce any coal-tar derivative we need.

Toluol

Another "coal-carbonization" product, which we had a hard time producing during the last World War but can now turn out in tremendous quantities, is toluol. Like phenol, it is a benzene homologue.

This substance is of paramount importance in wartime because TNT, the most powerful of high explosives, cannot be made without it. Produced by the action of nitric acid on toluol, TNT is the ideal shell-filler; for in addition to its great power it has the important advantage of being relatively safe to manufacture, load and transport. So far, no other explosive has been developed which possesses all these qualities; the next best explosive to TNT is a mixture containing that very substance. No wonder, then, that we used over 6,000,000 gallons of toluol in the last war!

Not all of it went into TNT, however. Toluol was used also in making khaki dyes, certain important pharmaceuticals, such as saccharine, and a large number of organic chemicals.

Peacetime uses also include paints, varnishes, enamels and stains, and normally consume about 20,000,000 gallons a year in the United States. About nine-tenths of this is produced at home—most of it as a by-product of the coke ovens.

Our wartime needs of toluol far exceed this amount. The Government is now asking for as much as 150,000,000 gallons a year; but even by working overtime our coke ovens cannot supply that quantity. They have never produced much more than about 20,000,000 gallons in the past, and can now supply only 30,000,000 gallons. Consequently there would be danger of a serious shortage in toluol were it not for the fact that this substance can also be produced from petroleum.

This is not new. We made considerable quantities of toluol from petroleum cracking during the First World War; in fact, when the Armistice was signed in 1918, one plant in California was ready to operate at the rate of 4,000,000 gallons a year. And all during those four years of war toluol was separated from Borneo oils in substantial amounts for the making of TNT.

Today new processes make it possible to produce toluol from petroleum in much greater amounts and several new plants have come into being in the past year or so for this purpose.

The first barrel, from our first petroleum toluol refinery constructed in the emergency of the present war, was produced at the Houston, Texas, plant of Shell Oil Company—more than a month ahead of schedule. Construction of this plant began in September, 1940, and was continued day and night at the greatest possible speed, with the result that by the middle of December all was ready for production.

Over 2,000,000 gallons of toluol a year (enough for 20,000,000 pounds of TNT) are being made at this one plant; and the Shell people have perfected a second process which can boost this output to 10,000,000 gallons a year if necessary; while their refineries in other sections of the country could add another 30,000,000 gallons.

But this is not all. Two plants engineered by the Universal Oil Products Company are making toluol from crude oil; and the Humble Oil & Refining Company, having received a contract from the War Department for the construction of a $10,000,000 plant, is ready to produce this essential material. Their plant, put into full and successful operation in September, 1941, has a capacity well above the originally planned 27,000,000 gallons a year.

Altogether four different units, now being built or already in operation, use a catalytic process for converting petroleum fractions by aromatization reaction into toluol.

Added to the toluol produced by aromatization will be that made by the solvent extraction type of process which, when all the proposed plants are in action, will probably yield 8,000,000 gallons a year.

All the other oil companies could make toluol, under license, by one of these methods by simply installing the equipment needed to supplement their present "cracking" apparatus; the raw materials would be the same as are now in use to produce good gasoline. The new equipment, it is true, would be expensive, but the actual production of toluol would be so cheap the costs of installation would soon be amortized.

Therefore, with ample supplies of crude oil and plants already equipped to produce toluol from this material, we should not have any trouble supplementing the supply obtained from the coke ovens —if we had only our own needs to consider.

The new plants now in construction or ready for use that will make toluol from petroleum will supply 70,000,000 gallons of the 100,000,000 now being demanded by the Government, and the remaining 30,000,-000 gallons can be supplied from coal carbonization in the coke ovens. But this country is the arsenal of democracy and may be called upon to send more and more TNT to Great Britain, Russia and our other allies. In that case a production of 100,000,000 gallons would not be enough and a shortage of this essential material would be inevitable.

In other words, our capacity is just sufficient, with all new plants in full production, to meet our present needs. The raw materials are here in abundance but the plants for their conversion into toluol could not be expanded overnight. Like synthetic rubber, like magnesium, like all of this war expansion program, the question is, first, where will the equipment come from at a time when every field and industry is clamoring for priority, and, second, how will we solve the bottleneck of adequately trained personnel?

[4]

Instruments of Mercy and Life-Saving Devices

FIRST on the strategic list of "life-savers" comes quinine, which, like rubber and tin, has long been imported from the East Indies and is unobtainable for the time being. Like rubber it is a native of South America and the long-range problem of its procurement can be solved by developing the cinchona trees now growing wild in Peru and Bolivia. For the immediate emergency, however, we shall have to depend on stock piles.

Kapok, needed for life-saving equipment and insulation, offers exactly the same problem, as it, too, has become almost an East Indian monopoly, although the trees can be grown in tropical America.

Cork, which has many of the same uses as Kapok, must still be imported from Spain, although eventually we may have large-yielding stands of cork oaks in California.

As for opium—coming mainly from the Near East—it does not yet offer a procurement problem; but should the shipments from Turkey cease we would have to rely on stock piles.

Iodine is quite a different matter, in spite of the fact that a large proportion of our domestic consumption has been imported from Chile. We can produce all and more than we need of this important germicide from the brine of oil wells.

A still brighter picture is presented by coconut-shell char (formerly necessary for gas masks), since it really is not essential any more and is only discussed in these pages because of its continued presence on the Army-Navy lists.

Aside from this material and iodine, our prospects of obtaining all we need of the strategic medicinals and materials for life-saving equipment are not too bright, and if this should prove to be a long war our chemists would be compelled to produce adequate substitutes.

Quinine

The Spanish Jesuits who followed their conquering countrymen to Peru were the first Europeans to discover the medicinal qualities of the bark of a tree indigenous to that country. Pulverized, this bark proved to be a specific against the malaria they encountered in the New World. The disease was not new to them; "ague" was a common complaint in southern Europe, but no medicine had been found there to combat it. Consequently, when the Countess of Chinchon, wife of the Governor of Peru, was stricken she was quite willing to try the strange remedy suggested by one of the Padres, and so successful was it in her case that the bark from which it was made received the name "Cinchona."

Over a hundred and ninety years had to pass, however, before the alkaloid, quinine, was isolated and its chemical characteristics determined, but it (with morphine and strychnine) was among the first substances studied by the pioneer scientists of the early nineteenth century.

So important was a specific for malaria to the inhabitants of southern Europe that quinine was soon being manufactured on a fairly large scale. There was constant trouble, however, in making the extract because the supply of cinchona bark was so irregular. Gathered by small groups of ignorant and careless natives from trees in the forests of the Andes, anywhere from 2500 to 9000 feet above sea-level, the bark had to be transported by mule-back many a weary mile before it started on its long journey across the Atlantic. Shipments, therefore, were sporadic and often included a large variety of barks.

Such an unsatisfactory supply of an essential remedy became so intolerable to one Paris physician, a Dr. Weddell, that he made an expedition to the forests of the Andes to obtain seeds of the cinchona tree, which were sown in the Jardin des Plantes in Paris in 1848, and in 1852 some of the plants were used to start the original, unsuccessful plantations in Java.

A few years later an Englishman, Sir Clements Markham, followed Dr. Weddell's example, but with a little more success. He carried back to England a large supply of cinchona plants (unfortunately not of the best species) which proved to be the foundation of still-flourishing plantations in India.

And finally, another Englishman—Charles Ledger, a resident of

Bolivia and Peru—was able through the efforts of his Indian servant to obtain a good supply of seeds, and from these grew trees producing the richest bark that had ever been encountered. One pound of these seeds—sent to London in 1865—were bought by the Dutch Government and shipped to Java on a warship; the other nine pounds went to India, where they were apparently lost. The "descendants" of the one pound taken to Java, however, and still known as "Ledgeriana," are today the world's principal source of cinchona bark for the manufacture of quinine. Grafted, now, with another species they produce a straighter tree, with a greater quinine yield. These trees have delicate blossoms, lavender, yellow and white, which grow in clusters and from which come the seeds so carefully guarded by the Dutch Government.

The Java plantations have for many years furnished over 90 percent of the cinchona needed for the world's supply of quinine—about 48,000,000 pounds of bark with an average content of 6 percent of quinine.

Most of the latter has been manufactured in Europe, some in this country and some at the government-owned factory at Bandoeng, Java. The factories in Germany, Switzerland, France, Italy and Holland have been closed for some time because no bark has been shipped to them from Java in recent times.

Cinchona trees are grown on a small scale in Formosa, where they are generally poor; and to a large extent in India, where most of them belong to a species yielding not more than 3 percent quinine. There are a few plantations of the better species in their native lands, Bolivia and Peru, Ecuador and Colombia; and a few in Jamaica, Central America, Brazil and the Philippines. The United States Government in 1940 sent one thousand plants to Rio de Janeiro, but unfortunately they were badly placed and will probably not be prolific.

About 97 percent of the world's production of quinine, as well as that of cinchona bark, has for some years been controlled by the Kina-Bureau, composed of a group of Java planters and a small number of European manufacturers. We imported 3,851,000 pounds of the bark in the first nine months of 1940, and 96 percent of that amount came from the Dutch East Indies—which shipped us 2,395,000 pounds in September alone. The loss of the Netherlands Indies to Japan has, of course, completely shut us out of supplies from that important area.

A protracted stoppage in supplies of this bark would be a serious

Cinchona Bark: United States Imports for Consumption, by
Principal Sources, in Specified Years, 1929 to 1940

	1929	1932	1936	1937	1938	1939	1940[a]
Latin America:			QUANTITY (1,000 POUNDS)				
Ecuador	—	11	44	22	6	26	19
Colombia	—	—	2	4	—	11	51
Guatemala	—	—	—	—	—	2	135
Peru	2	—	—	—	—	—	—
Nicaragua	—	b	—	—	—	—	3
Total Latin American countries	2	11	46	26	6	39	208
Other countries:							
Netherlands Indies	—	29	128	1,414	1,343	1,984	5,210
Netherlands	1,942	1,098	1,851	397	—	—	—
All other	16	1	26	—	b	7	—
Total imports: Quantity	1,960	1,139	2,051	1,837	1,349	2,030	5,418

matter were there no adequate substitute for the treatment of malarial
fever, which is a constant menace not only in the tropics but in many
other parts of the world, including the southeastern United States.
Fortunately atabrine, developed in Germany and now controlled by
our Government through Sterling Products Inc., is considered a satisfactory substitute for quinine and is being manufactured in this country as a reserve in case of shortage. License to manufacture has been
granted to the well-known pharmaceutical manufacturer, Merck &
Company. There is considerable agitation in Congress and elsewhere
seeking to have the controlling patents thrown open to all concerns
who are interested in producing the product.

For many years our scientists had been trying to discover a synthetic
product to replace this essential medicine; and their efforts led to the
development not only of remedies for other diseases but to a whole
field of chemical industry. For it was an attempt on the part of Perkins
to synthesize quinine by the oxidation of aniline that resulted in the
first coal-tar dye which was the cornerstone of the modern organic
chemical industry.

The many vegetable remedies used by the American Indians for
intermittent fever, and subsequently by the colonists, have been
thoroughly studied; but none of them has proved a real cure for
"chills and fever." It is reported that certain of the "sulfa" drugs
(promin and sulfadiazine) may be regarded as substitutes for quinine
in the treatment of malaria. But atabrine is the only one that has been
tried on a large scale.

Cinchona Bark: *Continued*

	1929	1932	1936	1937	1938	1939	1940[a]
			VALUE (1,000 DOLLARS)				
Latin America:							
Ecuador	—	1	3	3	1	3	2
Colombia	—	—	b	b	—	1	6
Guatemala	—	—	—	—	—	b	11
Peru	b	—	—	—	—	—	—
Nicaragua	—	b	—	—	—	—	b
Total Latin American countries	b	1	3	3	1	4	19
Other countries:							
Netherlands Indies	—	9	49	585	587	852	2,272
Netherlands	549	348	688	173	—	—	—
All other	3	b	5	—	b	1	—
Total imports:							
Value	552	358	745	761	588	857	2,291
Unit value (cents per pound)	28.2	31.5	36.3	41.5	43.6	42.2	42.3
			PERCENT OF TOTAL UNITED STATES IMPORTS				
Latin America:							
Quantity	0.1	0.9	2.2	1.4	0.5	1.9	3.8
Value	.1	.2	.4	.4	.1	.5	.8

[a] Preliminary.   b Not over 500.

SOURCE: Compiled from official statistics of the U. S. Department of Commerce.

With cinchona bark from Java no longer available, we shall depend more largely on our Latin-American neighbors to supply us with bark from their all-too-few plantations, supplemented perhaps with the bark of wild cinchona trees. The wild bark is only half as rich in quinine as that of the plantation "Ledger" trees of Java, but these native trees of the Andean slopes might be cultivated to produce enough in an emergency to fill our essential needs. Also, efforts are being made to develop more cinchona plantations in Central America. One plant in the United States is reported to be turning out limited quantities of quinine from bark imported from Central America.

Guatemala (where *C. ledgeriana* was planted three years ago) and Nicaragua, as well as Colombia, Ecuador and Peru, furnished cinchona bark to the United States during 1940. Two thousand pounds received from Guatemala in 1939 were the first to come from that country, which sent us 135,000 pounds in 1940. Colombia has been exporting small amounts since 1931, but the 51,000 pounds received here in 1940 were nearly double the amount received during all the other years.

Cinchona Bark: Production in Principal Producing Countries
of Latin America and of the World, in Specified Years, 1929 to 1938

COUNTRY	1929	1932	1936	1937	1938
	QUANTITY (1,000 POUNDS)				
Latin America:[a][b]					
Bolivia	303	400	1,964	2,132	1,950
Peru	161	186	146	223	185
Ecuador	[c]	61	170	162	[c]
Colombia	—	4	27	119	2
Total Latin American countries	464	651	2,307	2,636	2,137
Other countries:					
Netherlands Indies	26,213	22,372	22,064	23,287	24,665
British India	126[a]	1,669	1,764	2,086	1,984[d]
Total[e]	26,803	24,692	26,135	28,009	28,786
	PERCENT OF TOTAL				
Latin America	1.7	2.6	8.8	9.4	7.4

[a] Exports.   [b] Includes cascarilla.   [c] Not available.   [d] Estimated.
[e] Total of above principal producing countries only.
SOURCE: Compiled from official trade statistics of Latin America and from Export Crops
of the Netherlands Indies.

The same is true of Ecuador, which shipped us 19,400 pounds in 1940;
and that year Nicaragua, which had exported a small amount in 1932,
sent us 2,200 pounds.

Besides encouraging these "good neighbors" to cultivate the
cinchona bark, we have had our own Department of Agriculture ex-
perimenting for several years in raising *Cinchona ledgeriana* in Puerto
Rico under control conditions. As a result of these efforts, a high-
yielding strain of bark has been developed, and this plantation may
prove very useful within a few years.

For the present, however, cinchona bark from Latin America is
still both limited and low in quinine content; so it is not likely that
the entire production of all Central and South America will be adequate to meet any substantial part of our needs in the near future.

Exact figures for amounts now on hand are not available, but it is
known that late in 1941 a war reserve of quinine was being maintained by the Medical Departments of the United States Army, Navy
and Public Health Services.

Therefore our strategic position as regards quinine, while not spe-
cially favorable, is fairly secure, thanks to the chemist.

Iodine

Named from the Greek word for "violet" in allusion to the color of its vapor, iodine is a purple-black, crystalline solid which volatilizes easily at ordinary temperature, giving off an odor somewhat like chlorine. It has a potent germicidal action and is corrosive.

Widely but sparingly distributed in nature, this element seldom occurs free and is very apt to be found combined with silver, mercury and lead (as in the case of ores found in Mexico, Chile and Spain) or with lead alone (as in several South American ores) or with zinc (as in Silesia). It is also present in kelp—from which it is extracted in Scotland, France, Japan and Norway; in sea water and in Russian and American oil brines.

The percentage of iodine in these brines is so small that it is amazing to find that they are now one of the principal commercial sources of the element. They have put us in the second place as iodine producers. The brines contain only one one-hundred-and-fiftieth as much iodine as the Chilean nitrate liquors of which the content is 8 grams per litre. These used to furnish about 85 percent of the world's total supply of a thousand or more tons of iodine a year.

This small tonnage indicates the amount of iodine required to meet world demand. Like mercury, platinum, antimony and nickel, iodine is used in very small quantities. It is of strategic importance principally because of its use in hospitals. There are more potent antiseptics on the market now, it is true, but none of them has stood the tests of time and practical experience through which iodine has proved its usefulness. It should be said, however, that preliminary information indicates that the so-called "sulfa" drugs performed wonders in the treatment of the wounded at Pearl Harbor, and probably this group of comparatively new compounds may greatly reduce losses due to infection.

In addition to its medicinal applications, iodine is essential to a nation at war, in the production of sensitizing solutions used in the manufacture of photographic films, plates and papers. For this purpose it cannot be replaced; and these solutions play a very important part in aerial warfare.

There are other commercial applications of iodine which have indirect strategic significance—such as its use as a chemical reagent in the laboratory, in various organic compounds and dyes, as cattle-feed and in fertilizers for soils low in iodine.

The use of iodine in feeds and fertilizers is of fairly recent date, but it has long been the practice to add potassium iodide to common salt as a precaution against goiter; and the same substance has also been added to the drinking water in certain districts where there is a known deficiency of iodine in the soils and in the general diet of the people.

For this highly important function, too, there is no substitute, so that iodine is really fundamental to the good health of the nation at peace or at war. It is fortunate for us that we could produce sufficient quantities of this element from the brines of abandoned oil wells to meet all our needs if, by any chance, we could no longer import the Chilean iodine, which now covers over half our normal annual consumption of about a million pounds.

Imports in 1940 (all crude) totaled 1,244,146 pounds, six times those of 1936, and domestic production during that year continued the increase begun in 1937, when our output was 299,286 pounds.

As a matter of fact, the recovery of iodine in this country depends to a very large extent upon the market price, so that if suspension of imports should cause a sufficient increase in price, profitable recovery of iodine could probably be increased to about 500 tons annually—or the equivalent of our yearly domestic consumption.

Since the United States sales agency of the Chilean iodine producers consistently maintains a minimum stock on hand of 1,000 metric tons —or two years' normal supply—there would always be enough iodine on hand, if imports were cut off, to see us through while our domestic production facilities were being increased.

Moreover, we understand that the producers of Chilean iodine have promised the United States Army to keep no less than one million pounds of Chilean iodine in stock, in approved warehouses at easily accessible points—and at no cost to our Government.

Iodine, then, is on the critical list not because it threatens to offer a serious procurement problem, but because we do normally import a good part of our needs, and because, for its important applications there are no substitutes.

Germany, which depends on foreign sources for all its iodine requirements, after reducing consumption to a minimum and trying various means of secondary recovery, was forced to develop substitutes. The only really successful one has already been accepted as standard by the German army. For industrial purposes, especially photography, iodine itself must still be used.

Crude Iodine Imported for Consumption in the United States, 1936-40

Year	Pounds	Value
1936	592,217	$ 558,326
1937	1,967,148	1,784,491
1938	570,532	464,303
1939	200,000	168,238
1940	1,244,146	1,296,181

Opium

Opium has a sinister sound, suggesting Oriental wickedness, but to a pain-racked sufferer it spells release and blessed oblivion. And to a country at war sufficient supplies of morphine and codein, the opium derivatives, are as necessary as guns and bullets.

Obtained from the white poppy, which is probably indigenous to both southern Europe and western Asia, opium (dried poppy juice) is associated in most people's minds with China, where it used to be produced in enormous quantities, but the principal world source of this substance is Turkey, with Persia second and Yugoslavia third. India also produces large amounts, and Russia some.

Theoretically, the *Papaver somniferum* could be cultivated in any region where there is not an excessive rainfall and the climate is temperate or subtropical; but the yield is smaller in temperate than in tropical regions and it is not profitable to grow opium poppies unless labor and land are both cheap and abundant.

Labor must be cheap to make opium profitable because it is gathered by hand and its collection requires two separate operations. First, after the heat of the day has passed, cuts must be made in the poppy capsules; then, the next morning, the exuded juice is collected by scraping the capsule with a knife and transferring the secreted juice to a poppy-leaf. This is placed in the shade to dry for several days.

To obtain morphine and the other derivatives (all alkaloids) opium is dried and ground and the alkaloid extracted by a suitable solvent.

Yugoslavian and Persian opium, being the purest and containing the largest percentage of morphia, are generally used to produce these medicinals, and most of this opium is normally imported from Belgrade.

Should we find it impossible to receive shipments from either the Near East or Asia our situation with regard to opium might be quite serious. Domestic manufacturers, however, had prepared for just such an emergency, with the approval of the Treasury Department—responsible for the enforcement of the narcotic laws. About three years' supply had been stored by the outbreak of the present war. Since that time imports have been keeping pace with consumption, so that the three-year stocks of raw opium are still available, as well as those of finished derivatives held by the manufacturers, wholesale dealers and retailers.

A much smaller stock is held by the War Department. In 1925 the Surgeon General of the Army was given authority to accept and store in reserve all stocks of opium or its derivatives suitable for medical use, which should be seized or confiscated by the Narcotics Division.

The sum total of these supplies is probably more than sufficient for all military purposes—and perhaps also for civilian use.

Cork

All the cork in the world used to come from an area about the size of New Jersey, which extends in a narrow belt along the shores of the Mediterranean—1,000 miles of it on the southern coast of Spain and the northern shores of Africa. Also, there are important cork stands along the coast of Portugal. The evergreen trees with the spongy bark consistently refused to grow in large quantities anywhere else except in the southwest section of the United States—in spite of many attempts to establish cork plantations in this country, and in several others. Now, there are 2,000 cork oaks in southern California and plans were made to distribute 10,000 seedlings there in 1941.

Even if the trees can flourish in California, it will take some time to make their cultivation pay dividends, for the bark is never stripped from the trees before they are fifteen years old, and often not before they are thirty.

After the first stripping, they can be stripped every nine or ten years for the hundred and fifty years of their lives, and the quality of the cork improves with each stripping. Thus the man who starts a cork plantation today is making an investment for his children, grand-children and great-grandchildren.

In the meantime, he can raise pigs for a quick turn-over, as they thrive on cork acorns and root out all underbrush around the trees. Or he can plant a vineyard below his stands while he waits for the trees to reach their average height of about 30 feet.

When the time finally comes for the first stripping a rough, unequal bark is taken off: this is "virgin cork," useful as a tanning material and for insulations, and frequently used for making the rustic trim-mings of conservatories and ferneries. Ten years later the bark has considerably improved, but it is still too coarse to be used except for such things as floats for nets; but by the time the trees are stripped the third time a cork is obtained which can be used in the manufacture of an almost endless variety of products found in such diversified objects as those in automobiles and refrigerators. For this valuable bark has a unique combination of properties, including buoyancy, compressibility, resilience, resistance to moisture and liquid penetra-tion, frictional quality, low thermal conductivity, ability to absorb vibration, and stability.

Its most obvious use is, of course, in stoppers for bottles and other vessels containing liquids—usually called "corks" even though they are now often made of glass or some plastic. This was for a long time the principal use of cork. Now, less than 5 percent of the cork used in the United States goes into bottle stoppers, floats and buoys, fishing-tackle bobbers, penholder grips, disks, balls, handles, and such com-monplace products. The bulk of this material is manufactured into cork board, cork pipe-covering, and granulated cork for loose-fill insulation.

Cork board, with its property of absorbing vibration, is used in the base of heavy machinery; and for correcting poor acoustics and help-ing to control the temperature in planes and tanks, as well as in theatres and restaurants.

That is one reason why cork is an essential material today. Another is its use in life-buoys, belts and jackets, and in life-boat equipment and other life-saving apparatus, so important in time of war, especially in naval warfare.

Also of strategic value are cork gaskets and floats in the carburetors

Corkwood or Cork Bark, Unmanufactured: United States Imports
for Consumption, by Principal Sources, in Specified Years, 1929 to 1940

COUNTRY	1929	1932	1936	1937	1938	1939	1940ª
			QUANTITY (1,000 POUNDS)				
Portugal	30,632	14,286	43,107	68,755	25,999	33,836	82,614
Algeria b	21,296	8,628	12,456	19,306	10,004	12,987	5,170
Spain	16,232	3,495	17,386	14,367	7,231	10,064	15,926
Morocco	7,500	2,382	1,871	9,047	3,689	5,682	3,089
All other	14,982	808	40	3,973	1,460	834	604
Total imports	90,642	29,599	74,860	115,448	48,383	63,403	107,403
			VALUE (1,000 DOLLARS)				
Portugal	1,294	397	1,509	2,414	784	917	2,037
Algeria b	792	169	355	741	234	290	142
Spain	611	86	447	407	251	286	390
Morocco	140	26	38	178	42	61	40
All other	403	6	5	80	35	12	9
Total imports:							
Value	3,240	684	2,354	3,820	1,346	1,566	2,618
Unit value (cents per pound)	3.6	2.3	3.1	3.3	2.8	2.5	2.4

ª Preliminary.
b Classification includes Tunisia prior to 1936; no imports from Tunisia since 1936.
SOURCE: Compiled from official statistics of the U. S. Department of Commerce.

of automobiles and planes, non-slip treads on the wing-walks of planes,
and insulation of electrical equipment.

For textile machinery and equipment cork is essential, as it is for
lubricating equipment and bearings, and for the measuring, handling
and dispensing of gases and liquids.

Consequently a shortage of this material in a major emergency
would entail serious difficulties. There exist cellular plastics and plastic
boards which in some respects can be used to replace cork in a few of
its uses; and for others, such as stoppers, glass can be used; but the
only substitute available for one of cork's most important applications,
life-saving equipment, is kapok, and that too is on the strategic list.
Even the synthetic rubber that might be used is simply not available
in sufficient quantities.

There are, as we have said, several stands of cork trees in California.
One commercial stripping was made in 1940, and the bark was of very

good quality, but it will be years before this small beginning can bear sufficient fruit to meet our full requirements.

It is to be hoped, therefore, that we have been laying in a supply of this material over and above our usual annual consumption of 100,000 to 150,000 metric tons a year. No figures are available on this, but we do know that in May of 1940, in spite of large imports for the year, stocks of cork on hand were insufficient to meet production schedules. Cork has since been placed under industry-wide control; on or after June 12, 1941, each supplier of cork was required to set aside his entire stock in all forms as a reserve out of which the director of priorities could make allocations, for defense orders.

The American cork industry has been cooperating fully with the Government agencies and stocks have been increasing steadily, with the result that it was reported late in 1941 that current inventories more than equaled estimated defense requirements for the next two years. Since we have entered the war that picture may have changed appreciably, but no figures are as yet available.

Kapok

When the Dutch began to colonize the East Indies, early in the seventeenth century, they noticed that the natives, particularly of Java, made use of a floss obtained from certain trees growing nearly all over the island. Tall and gaunt, with sparse branches shooting out at right angles from the trunk, these kapok trees were a striking characteristic of the Javanese landscape. Hanging from the narrow branches of these spindly giants (some of them a hundred feet high) were pods, five to seven inches long, containing the silky floss which the islanders found so useful for cushions and bedding.

Though the colonists were not slow to make use of the kapok, they did not think of bringing any back to Holland until the middle of the nineteenth century—probably because, being so light, the floss took up too much space on the small merchant ships of that period.

When in 1893 the floss was exhibited at the World's Columbian Exposition in Chicago, the makers of mattresses and upholstered furniture realized at once its practicability, and kapok became almost overnight an important article of world trade. Textile manufacturers were also keenly interested, hoping these lustrous fibers might prove

Unmanufactured Kapok: United States Imports for Consumption, by Principal Sources, in Specified Years, 1929 to 1940

	1929	1932	1936	1937	1938	1939	1940[a]
			QUANTITY (LONG TONS)				
Latin America:							
Ecuador	25	1	265	251	347	472	384
Dominican Republic	—	18	48	36	—	35	85
Peru	—	—	—	1	b	8	—
Brazil	8	b	20	23	16	8	13
Cuba	—	—	—	—	45	—	—
All other	—	b	5	—	—	2	—
Total Latin American countries	33	19	338	311	408	525	482
Other countries:							
Netherlands Indies	6,799	7,535	13,951	10,905	5,416	8,237	7,122
British India (including Burma)	209	9	45	28	93	346	2
Philippines	2	10	342	446	305	227	148
Netherlands	2	195	15	—	—	—	—
Germany	45	—	—	—	—	—	—
All other	43	—	8	20	32	44	46
Total imports	7,133	7,768	14,699	11,710	6,254	9,379	7,800

[a] Preliminary.

[b] Less than ½ ton.

SOURCE: Compiled from official statistics of the U. S. Department of Commerce.

to be a satisfactory substitute for always-expensive silk, as well as an improvement upon cotton, for kapok has the warmth of wool. It was found, however, that the fibers were too brittle for spinning; its only use was as a substitute for goose feathers or hair as fillers for bedding and upholstery. Cheap and plentiful, kapok proved a very practical material for those purposes.

It now has another use, of more interest to us in wartime. Due to its low specific gravity kapok is ideal for life-saving equipment, and therefore it is of prime importance to nations engaged in the present sea war.

Besides being used in the familiar life-jackets seen on every ship— some of them contain cork and not kapok—the East Indian fibers are now being employed to make a buoyant waistcoat to be worn by the crews of ships plying in dangerous waters. Men on torpedoed ships do not always have time to put on life-jackets, however easy they may be to get into, and these jackets cannot be worn all the time, as they

Kapok: Exports from Principal Exporting Countries of
Latin America and of the World, in Specified Years, 1929 to 1938

	1929	1932	1936	1937	1938
	QUANTITY (LONG TONS)				
Latin America:					
Brazil	347	181	160	256	388
Peru	1	—	16	2	10
Ecuador	33	8	421	328	a
Dominican Republic	37	26	85	57	82
Costa Rica	145	—	—	—	—
Total Latin American countries	563	215	682	643	—
Other countries:					
Netherlands Indies b	17,154	18,204	27,447	18,233	15,704
Indo-China	742	1,172	3,025	3,133	3,713
British India	1,906	1,202	1,540	993	1,638
French Africa	2,162	903	1,115	1,254	1,522
Ceylon	432	303	409	395	577
Philippines	325	359	987	1,111	520
All other	62	106	178	337	549
World total	23,346	22,464	35,383	26,099	24,703 c
	PERCENT OF WORLD TOTAL				
Latin America	2.4	1.0	1.9	2.5	—

a Not available, but probably larger than in 1937.
b Gross weight in terms of cleaned kapok.
c Not including Ecuador.
SOURCE: Compiled from official trade statistics of the Latin American countries shown, and from De Landbouwexportgewassen van Nederlandsch Indie.

interfere with the freedom of movement necessary to men engaged in active duties. A kapok-filled waistcoat, on the other hand, which will support 19 pounds in water, can be worn under an ordinary jacket, and has the further advantage of keeping the wearer warm in inclement weather.

All aviators wear kapok-filled garments, and both planes and tanks are lined with it. Not only does it shut out a certain amount of noise but it also serves as a protection against thermal influences.

Well over 90 percent of the world's total production of kapok has always come from Java, though the trees are cultivated also in British India, Malaya and the Philippines. In the present world situation it is most fortunate for us that the kapok tree grows wild in parts of Central and South America and the West Indies.

We have been importing small amounts of it, for the past few years, from Brazil, Peru, Ecuador, the Dominican Republic and Cuba. These imports have not been enough to make any real difference— about 500 tons compared to the average of 9,000 tons we usually import from Java—but they have served as an indication of where we might be able to get kapok in an emergency. In 1940 about 325,000 seedlings were planted in private nurseries in Guatemala and about 195,000 in El Salvador.

It will take six years for these trees to be in production, and even by increasing the harvest from the kapok trees growing wild in other parts of Latin America it will not be possible to obtain anywhere near the amount of kapok we need.

For the immediate future, therefore, kapok offers a serious procurement problem, and it is most unfortunate that the same is true of cork, which has identical strategic uses—uses for which no substitute is yet available. If the sea lanes are closed and our supplies of these materials become exhausted, it will be up to American chemists to "find a way."

Coconut-Shell Char

Coconut-shells really have no place on the Army-Navy list of critical materials, since they are no longer necessary as the raw material for the carbon used in gas masks.

Several countries in Europe have been making active carbon from hardwood ever since the last war and their plants were capable of turning out the gas-absorbing variety as well as the decolorizing carbons with which our manufacturers have been solely familiar.

It was not until the beginning of this war that we began to learn how to use the processes successfully practiced in Europe for twenty years. Our Government has had to spend several millions of dollars to train the technicians and build the plants necessary to produce enough active carbon from our domestic hardwoods to equip our armed forces with gas protection.

Activated carbon is necessary also as a catalyst in the manufacture of phosgene (a war gas) and, luckily, the same domestic woods will make that carbon.

We have been "slow on the trigger" as far as activated carbon is concerned, but we are fortunate in having plenty of the raw material needed to make this essential product, so that we will probably not be called upon to save fruit pits, as we were in the last war, and none of the cargo space so badly needed for minerals should have to be filled with coconut-shells. A number of plants have been erected with government funds and will be operated by several of the leading chemical companies.

[5]

Clothes for the Soldier

Textiles

THE TEXTILES on the list of essential raw materials bring us to the larger question of the increasing importance of man-made fibers—a peculiarly twentieth-century phenomenon which may have economic results beyond our present immediate reckoning.

From the very dawn of history right down to our own generation men had to depend on natural fibers for their wearing apparel and other coverings. Wool, linen, silk and cotton—these alone could be woven into the materials which adorned the persons and the dwelling-places of mankind.

Today yarns can be made from glass, milk, rubber, oil, salt and air; cellulose, a natural product of cotton, can be prepared from wood; and silk, for many centuries the monopoly of certain moths, can now be "concocted" from coal and salt.

Silk

While, technically, the fibrous substances produced by many insects in the form of nests or webs are really silk, the one made by the mulberry silk-moth of China or some of its near relatives is the only silk used for manufacturing purposes.

These moths have been cultivated in China since very ancient times. As early as 2460 B.C. an empress showed marked interest in their culture and had the ladies of her court instructed in the use of the silken fibers. And knowledge of this art remained a Chinese secret and an aristocratic prerogative for many generations.

Indeed, it was not until the third century of our era that sericulture traveled by way of Korea to Japan, where it has flourished ever since. From there it spread slowly westward, as travelers became more frequent, and from Greece it was taken to ancient Rome and handed down to the modern Italians. Then a French king—in the sixteenth century—brought silkworms from Milan, and had them installed in the Rhone Valley, initiating what proved to be one of his country's most lucrative industries. England came next, with the advent of the Flemish weavers; and from there the notion of growing silkworms was carried to the American colonies, where several unsuccessful attempts were made to establish mulberry plantations.

Benjamin Franklin was interested in one of them; and the hope of starting a silk industry in this country has never been entirely abandoned. No one has succeeded, however, in making silkworms "pay" here, and it is not likely that they ever will, for the only places in which raw silk has ever been profitably produced have had abundant and very cheap labor—China, Japan, Bengal, Piedmont and the Levant.

Of these, Japan is by far the largest producer and was responsible for 75 percent of our imports of silk, which amounted to about 55,000,-000 pounds in 1930, or over half of the total world's supply. Since then, however, our imports have declined 30 percent, despite a 50 percent fall in price. This was due to the growing use of synthetic fibers; first, the various rayons and now, nylon, which wears twice as long as real silk. Consequently, a large portion of the millions of pounds of silk we used to import is no longer needed here. Now in rapid succession we are discovering new fibers—Vinyon, Aralac (the latter made from milk!), and the future of silk becomes more and more a question mark.

Silk, however, is on the list of essential materials because certain of its uses have definite strategic importance—such as insulation for wires and cables, powder bags (made from "waste silk") for heavy ammunition, and parachutes for flares and aviators. Seventy yards of silk are required for a parachute.

For most of these purposes, the substitutes of silk have been developed to a point where they can easily replace the natural product for all military uses, except possibly powder bags; and for these there would be a sufficient supply of waste silk—or they can and indeed are made of cotton. American women may experience a shortage of nylon stockings during the war, but our aviators will be sure to have plenty of parachutes, for the plant capacity for the production of this extremely useful substance is being greatly increased. DuPont has recently announced a further 25 percent expansion of its nylon capacity to 20,000,000 pounds yearly, to be effective by the end of 1942.

Consequently, although we cannot produce even a small proportion of the silk we need in this emergency, due to nylon, our strategic position with regard to this material is not serious.

Indeed, but for its great importance in the past, raw silk would not merit consideration as an essential raw material. We can do without silk, but Japan cannot do without buyers of that commodity, and when this war is over and she has lost her best customer, her people will find that their bid for conquest was more expensive than they calculated.

Wool

At just what point animal fiber ceases to be hair and becomes wool is impossible to determine, so we are justified in saying that wool is the most important of the animal fibers. The health and comfort of the nation are dependent upon an adequate supply of this material at all times, and during a war wool clothing is absolutely necessary for the armed forces. It is estimated that 19 pounds of wool are used in making a soldier's uniform.

The fact that certain animal hairs or fibers could be spun into threads which, in turn, could be woven into cloth for warm and comfortable clothing has been known for many centuries. First mentioned in written history by Pliny, the art of weaving wool was introduced by the Romans to the British Isles. It became the most important source of wealth to England and was brought by English colonists to the Western World.

When the Romans reached Britain they found sheep there and had only to teach the Britons the importance of these animals. The British colonists, on the contrary, found no sheep in America and had to import these wool-bearing animals—first to Jamestown in Virginia in 1609 and to Boston in 1633, and it was several years after the latter date before there were any mills in this country.

With the growth and development of the colonies, both sheep-raising and textile factories increased tremendously, but after the introduction of merino sheep into Australia, in the late eighteenth century, that country became the leading wool producer of the world, with an output of 938,000,000 pounds in 1938. Argentina and Uruguay, where merinos were introduced sometime later, also produce tremendous quantities of wool (385,000,000 and 121,000,000 pounds respectively in 1938) and are close runners-up for position as second to Australia.

In spite of our very large domestic production—441,897,000 pounds in 1939—we import over 40 percent of our annual consumption, buying not only from Australia, Argentina and Uruguay but also from the United Kingdom.

The Latin American countries do not produce the same kind of wool as that which comes from Australia, for the proportion of merino sheep in them is very small and it is only from those particular animals that fine apparel wool can be secured. Latin America does ship limited amounts of fine animal hair, coming from those relatives of the camel (alpaca, llama, and vicuña) that inhabit the Peruvian and Bolivian Andies; but these constitute a small proportion of the total wool shipped from South America. Most of it is of the coarser, carpet-grade wool.

All of the coarser grades of wool do not go into floor coverings. Some are mixed with the coarser grades of apparel wools to make special fabrics, blankets, and the less expensive woven fabrics and knit goods. The coarser apparel wools that have some luster are often blended with mohair in the making of light-weight summer suitings and dress goods, and for some upholstery fabrics. The medium grades of apparel wool—of which the United States is a large producer—go into ordinary suitings and dress goods. And the fine apparel wools, grown chiefly in Australia, are blended with alpaca, angora and cashmere (fine animal hairs) in the manufacture of special clothing and knit goods. Felts may be made of all grades of short wool.

In other words, without our imports from Australia we would be unable to manufacture the soft, light materials that are used in the best suitings and dress goods. We could still make plenty of the coarser and the everyday materials, as we buy the former grade of wool from Latin America and produce the latter type ourselves.

However, if our supplies from overseas are drastically curtailed, there might be, temporarily at least, a serious shortage in all wool, as our output might not be increased in time to meet the heavy demands caused by the war. The shortage, of course, would be felt by civilians only; our domestic capacity is probably ample for basic military needs. Production in this country has been increased since the beginning of the war; our wool clip in 1940 was the largest on record.

In addition, imports during that year were very heavy—212,909,000 pounds of wool and 2,200,000 pounds of alpaca and similar hair. Most of the hair came from Latin America and of the wool 122,000,000 pounds came from there, and for the first time over half of that amount was apparel wool. This means that clothing manufacturers here have been getting ready to do without Australian wool, though plans were made to bring large quantities of it to be stored here.

As a matter of fact, the beginning of 1941 found the entire textile industry prepared as never before. The depression years had taken their toll of both large and small manufacturers and the survivors had been wise enough to spend millions on new machinery as well as to place their mills on a more efficient basis.

As a result of all of this, the Quartermaster General was able to report, at the end of last November, that "for the first time in a grave national emergency its [this country's] armed forces are properly and adequately clothed." For this the mills share credit with wise officers in the War Department who, remembering the mistakes of the last World War, had listed all the available mills, had correct specifications and size schedules all ready, and even knew the quantities needed.

As an illustration of the tremendous quantities of various textiles involved, this is what the armed forces had bought by the end of November 1941, estimated to be a year's needs of the men then in the Army, with 50 percent reserve supplies in storage or camps—and all promptly delivered without strain on the industry, which can treble these shipments in 1942:

4,724,520	Suits of white clothing
14,955,585	Khaki trousers
141,047,000	Yards khaki cloth for suits
80,052,000	” ” ” ” caps, shirts, breeches, etc.
14,987,160	Yards of 32-oz. Melton
61,855,469	Yards of 18-oz. Melton
41,450,000	” ” shirting flannel
4,328,343	Jackets

16,880,828	Khaki shirts
77,921,897	Socks of all kinds
65,809,250	Pieces of summer underwear
28,873,314	” ” winter ”
9,628,000	Blankets
18,000,000	Sheets
21,894,882	Towels
18,967,713	Neckties
29,077,019	Handkerchiefs
9,087,222	Leggings
4,972,000	Raincoats
1,400,000	Mackinaws
1,977,616	Barrack bags
147,661	Rolls of bedding for officers

The average civilian uses about 10 pounds of wool a year; the soldier in training requires about 75 pounds, and his "buddy" in active service over 50 pounds more. Because of the added protection aboard ships and at shore stations, the men in the Navy use less wool—only about 30 pounds a year per man.

These figures of course, are for our Army and Navy, which are the warmest clad in the world. Our Government requires the use of virgin wool only, in all military apparel. We can afford to be particular. All the Axis-held countries together can produce only 125,-000 tons of wool, while the annual crop available to the United Nations amounts to 2,000,000 tons.

Wool: United States Imports for Consumption by Types, Showing Share Supplied by Latin America, in Specified Years, 1929 to 1940

			SUMMARY				
COUNTRY AND TYPE	1929[a]	1932	1936	1937	1938	1939	1940[b]
		QUANTITY (1,000 POUNDS—CLEAN CONTENT)					
Latin America:							
Carpet wool	—	7,527	37,594	40,132	21,608	41,065	60,117
Apparel wool	23,268[c]	454	17,172	20,003	3,278	14,968	61,969
Total	—	7,981	54,766	60,137	24,886	56,033	122,086
All countries:							
Carpet wool	—	31,776	120,248	141,049	58,382	119,625	111,240
Apparel wool	60,435[c]	7,507	51,923	74,468	11,335	42,618	101,669
Total imports	—	39,283	172,171	215,517	69,717	162,243	212,909

Wool: *Continued*

COUNTRY AND TYPE	1929[a]	1932	1936	1937	1938	1939	1940[b]
	PERCENT OF TOTAL UNITED STATES IMPORTS—QUANTITY						
Latin America:							
Carpet wool	—	23.7	31.3	28.5	37.0	34.3	54.0
Apparel wool	38.5	6.0	33.1	26.9	28.9	35.1	61.0

[a] Clean content of carpet wool not available in 1929.
[b] Preliminary.
[c] Includes some wool now classified as carpet wool.
SOURCE: Compiled from official statistics of the U. S. Department of Commerce.

Wool: Production in Principal Producing Countries, in Specified Years 1929 to 1938

COUNTRY	1929	1933	1936	1937	1938
	QUANTITY (1,000,000 POUNDS)				
Latin America:					
Argentina	323	348	350	380	385
Uruguay	135	101	112	128	121
Chile	33	32	25	34	31
All other	56	54	85	84	90
Total Latin American countries	547	535	572	626	627
Other countries:					
Australia	925	847	990	1,014	938
United States	363	429	426	433	436
New Zealand	222	279	295	314	305
Union of South Africa	312	255	251	230	240
Canada and Newfoundland	21	19	19	19	19
Europe [a]	912	638	655	783	837
Asia [b]	230	223	316	310	314
Africa [c]	88	69	115	121	115
World total	3,620	3,294	3,639	3,850	3,830
	PERCENT OF WORLD TOTAL				
Latin America	15.1	16.2	15.7	16.3	16.4

[a] Including the Soviet Union in Europe and Asia.
[b] Excluding the Soviet Union in Europe and Asia.
[c] Excluding the Union of South Africa.
NOTE:—The statistics for Latin American countries include the various related specialty hairs.
SOURCE: Bulletins, National Association of Wool Manufacturers.

Leather

Anyone who has ever had to walk for very long in a pair of uncomfortable shoes will appreciate the importance of all types of hides and tanning materials, for the quality of the former and the proper blending of the latter determine the comfort as well as the longevity of shoe leather.

To a nation at war both of these qualities are of real concern, for soldiers and sailors must have comfortable shoes if they are to render efficient service and those shoes must be able to take plenty of punishment. Consequently, in a national emergency hides, skins and tanning materials immediately become essential raw materials.

When we speak of hides we mean the pelts of horses and buffaloes as well as those of cattle; "skins" come from the smaller animals—calves, sheep, goats. Of the hides, those from steer and cow, being the toughest, are made into sole and belting leather (the extra-large ones into upholstery); light cowhides are split into "side leather" for shoe uppers and for hand luggage; while bullhides go into chrome sole leather and upholstery leather.

As for skins, those used for shoe uppers, handbags, gloves and bookbindings are calf, soft and pliant with a fine grain, tight in texture, and goat, tough and tight-grained. Sheepskins, used for shoe linings and gloves, are extremely porous, except in the case of still-born or less-than-one-month-old lambs, whose skins are made into the best-quality kid gloves.

In spite of the fact that we are the largest single producer of hides in the world we import about one-third of the hides we need; half of the calfskins, nearly all of the goatskins and about two-thirds of the sheepskins used. The largest percentage of hides comes from Argentina, home of the "Frigorificos," the second largest from Canada, and a considerable amount of buffalo hides from British India. That country is the largest producer of goatskins in the world, and, with China, supplies most of our imports. Canada is responsible for the largest number of calfskins we import. From Aden come all the mocha-skins; and Australia is the sole source of kangaroo and wallaby skins. Sheepskins are particularly a New Zealand product, though we import them from several other sources. In fact, the list of countries from which skins are sent to the United States in normal times includes Uganda, Zanzibar, Nigeria, Madagascar, Tunisia, Morocco,

Algeria, Haiti, Barbados, Java, Hejaz, Poland, Finland and Norway.

Should all of these sources be denied us, a serious problem of supply and demand would present itself until our domestic output could be sufficiently increased. This would mean a civilian shortage only, as we could easily meet our strictly military needs, and the existing substitutes for leather could cover civilian demands while domestic production was being expanded.

We have considerably increased our imports from South America, thereby greatly benefiting those countries, which used to sell large quantities to Europe; and as long as the shipping lanes remain open and cargo space is available this source of supply will prove plentiful. From August, 1939, to September, 1940, Latin American countries supplied 60 percent of the cattle hides dry or dry-salted, and 87 percent of the much larger amount of cattle hides wet-salted, imported into the United States.

Individual tanners—needing calfskins and certain kinds of sheepskins—are having a hard time, but our national situation, as far as hides are concerned, involves no problem at the moment, even allowing for the increased demands.

Tanning Materials

Some of those far-away countries which supply hides and skins for the American leather industry also supply tanning materials—as in the case of Indian nuts and Madagascar barks—but they are not the only ones responsible for our shoes and handbags, gloves and luggage. Asia Minor and Greece, where valonia grows; Italy, where the sumac abounds; Natal, rich in wattle; and Venezuela, home of certain pods —all these contribute valuable tanning materials.

Tannin—from the Latin word *tannare,* meaning "oak bark"—is an acid abundantly found in a very large number of plants and may be secreted in their bark, wood, roots, leaves, seed-pods or fruit. So many, indeed, are the tannins found in nature that their number has never been determined, nor has the constitution of those familiar to us ever been satisfactorily analyzed. Some things, however, they all have in common—namely, a powerful astringency, solubility in water, the property of forming insoluble compounds with gelatine or gelatinous tissues, and that of forming blacks with iron.

Some tannin-producing materials are indigenous to the United

States—the oak, chestnut oak and hemlock, for instance, sumac leaves and chestnut woods. That is why the tanning industry in this country was originally concentrated in Pennsylvania and New Hampshire, where the oaks were plentiful, in New York, Michigan and Wisconsin, abounding in hemlocks, and in the South where many chestnuts grew.

Unfortunately, we were, for generations, so careless of our forests that our stands of hemlock and oak have been depleted to the point that we must now import these barks, and a blight has carried off most of our chestnut trees.

Our most important import is Argentine quebracho, "the ax-breaker," so hard that it is "almost like a vegetable iron," turns the edges of hard steel tools and breaks the teeth of circular saws. It will not float, and weighs about eighty pounds to the cubic foot.

This natural monopoly of South America is controlled by a few powerful and highly organized companies in Argentina and Paraguay, the two countries where it grows in commercial quantities—rarely, however, more than four or five trees to an acre. The ax-breaker needs plenty of room! Of these companies the most important is the Forestal Land, Timber and Railway Company of Argentina, spoken of as "La Forestal."

Two young German tanners, Carlos and Albert Hartneck, founded this company in 1880. They had noticed that the water near a certain sawmill became a deep red when quebracho sawdust was deposited in it, and they conceived the idea that this discoloration might be due to tannic acid; which proved to be the case when samples of the water were tested in Europe. So, buying quebracho land in the Chaco, the brothers began by exporting the wood to Le Havre in France. Nearly twenty years later, in cooperation with Renner of Hamburg, they erected an extract plant in the Province of Santa Fé and by 1902 were producing 7,800 tons of quebracho extract a year. In 1904 they became associated with the Brothers Portais of Buenos Aires, owners of tremendous quebracho lands, and the new company was called the "Compañia Forestal del Chaco," which became "La Forestal Land, Timber and Railway Company" when, in 1906, it was taken over by a British concern.

Quebracho, used principally on sole and cattle-hide leather for harnesses and belting, is one of the cheapest as well as one of the best tanning materials for these types of leather, due to its large tannin content and to the fact that it is the wood of the tree, not just the bark, which is so rich in the acid.

This is obtained—as are most tanning materials—by leaching the wood (or the bark or leaves) with hot water and then condensing the resulting liquor until it contains at least 25 percent tannin. It can then be marketed in liquid form or further evaporated until the extract is either solid or powder.

In the case of wattle, another important material, which we now import from South Africa and which contains 35 percent tannin, the extract can be marketed most cheaply in solid form. "Wattle" is really the barks of several species of the acacia indigenous to Australia, where it was originally used to bind bundles together, as willow wattles were used in England. About 1880 some of these acacia trees were planted in Natal, and from that country has come the bulk of the wattle bark of commerce for the last twenty years. Later plantations were started in New South Wales, Victoria, Tasmania, Queensland and New Zealand. In other words, the world supply of wattle is under British control.

The other tanning materials we import include several from the Malay Archipelago: myrobalans, the unripe fruit of various species of *Terminalia;* mangrove cutch, an extract made from *Rhizophora,* a mangrove tree, now also grown in British North Borneo and the Philippine Islands; and gambier, the leaves and twigs of the shrub *Unicaria gambier.* Also valonia, the cups and beards of acorns from *Quercus ægilops,* an oak indigenous to Greece, Asia Minor and Palestine; gallnuts, leaves and twigs of *Quercus infectoria* of China; divi-divi, the pods of *Cæsalpinia coriaria* of Venezuela, Colombia and Mexico; mangrove bark from Madagascar, East Africa and Borneo; and sumac leaves from Sicily.

Of these only sumac—of which we have plenty—and wattle can be grown in the United States. There are no commercial plantations of wattle, but certain of the trees have been grown successfully in California and there is ample evidence of their adaptability to the soil and climatic conditions not only of that region but also of Arizona, New Mexico, eastern Texas and Florida. In other words, wattle could be cultivated in the United States in areas readily accessible for commercial purposes. We could not, however, have large quantities of this material overnight. It takes seven years for the trees to produce tannin in sufficient amounts; then one acre of wattle trees yields about 6 tons of bark.

Since this is the foreign vegetable tannin possible to produce in the United States which would best meet the requirements of American tanners were imports shut off, it is earnestly to be hoped that some experimental plantations have been started by the United States Government.

For the other materials now imported we should have to find substitutes to supply our tremendous industry, normally consuming about 500,000,000 pounds of tanning materials a year, of which about one-half are brought in from abroad.

So far no satisfactory substitutes are on the market, but there is a process using chrome salts which is now employed in tanning practically all shoe upper leather as well as that for gloves and garments. By the chrome salt method the leather is tanned in a much shorter time than by vegetable tannins, and chrome leather is just as soft. In fact, chrome leather has the advantage of drying out soft from frequent wettings more satisfactorily than vegetable-tanned leather.

Our situation, then, should our supplies from overseas be stopped, would not be desperate, for we could produce the hides and some of the tanning materials needed, but the civilian population would probably have to put up with inferior products for some time.

Foreign and Domestic Tanning Materials
Used in American Tanning Industry

Material	Country of Origin	Average Amount (lb.) per Year Raw
Quebracho	Argentina	87,213,528
Chestnut	United States	*
Myrobalans	British India	28,446,133
Mangrove cutch	Malay Archipelago	*
Wattle bark	South Africa	19,777,769
Valonia	Turkey	18,328,233
Gambier	Malay Archipelago	3,839,392
Gallnuts	China	2,955,136
Divi-divi	Venezuela	350,000
Hemlock	United States	1,343,296
Sumac	Sicily; United States	7,767,857
Oak	United States	*

* Figures not available.

[6]

The Humble Fibers

THE THREE FIBERS, jute, manila hemp and sisal, which are listed as strategic materials, are all products of the tropics. Two of them, jute and manila hemp, come from the East and can be grown commercially in certain localities only. India produces most of the world's supply of jute, and the Philippine Islands most of the manila hemp. Sisal, on the other hand, is an "Occidental" and not quite so particular about its abode; a native of the peninsula of Yucatan it grows also in the West Indies, and has been introduced into Florida, Africa and the East Indies.

Jute

Jute is obtained from two plants, *Corchorus capsularis* and *Corchorus olitorius*. It is a bast fiber—the fiber that lies between the bark and the inner woody portion of the stem. From four to eight feet long, it is soft, pliable and easily spun and is the cheapest of all bast fibers. Indeed, except for cotton, jute is the most extensively used of all vegetable fibers.

There are two grades: long jute from the main part of the stem and jute butts from the thick woody butt of the stalk. Long jute is used principally in this country in the yarns called carpet warps (which are employed in the foundation of floor coverings and do not appear on the surface), wrapping-twines, upholstery-webbing and interlining for clothing; it is also used in making ropes for insulating electric power-transmission cables.

The butts are made into burlap, the major jute product employed the world over in bags for mill feed, wheat, flour and sugar, for baling

148

cotton and other merchandise, as a backing for linoleum, and for many other purposes.

A new use for jute has increased our demands for this material, already greatly enlarged by the defense program. Socks made of fiber are now issued to troops on Arctic duty, to be worn between their wool socks and their boots as an added protection against cold and dampness.

United States imports of jute consist largely of burlap. In 1940, for instance, we imported 225,000 long tons of burlap and 48,000 of jute fiber. Most of both of these items come from British India, with negligible amounts from the Far East.

Since no jute fiber is produced in the Western Hemisphere, British India is for all practical purposes our sole source of supply. Certain other fibers, however, grown in Latin America might be employed in some of the uses now requiring jute. In Brazil the caroa fiber is obtainable in large quantities and this and the Hibiscus flax are both reported to be acceptable substitutes for bagging. And cotton could certainly be used in this way. For the other uses of jute we shall have to turn to tropical America for other fibers that will answer the purpose even if they will not actually replace the jute.

Manila Fiber

The tonnage of manila fiber consumed in this country is not nearly as large as that of jute, but being essential for marine cordage manila hemp is the most important of all fibers from a strategic point of view. Due to its resiliency, its high tensile strength and its long life under all sorts of weather conditions, this material is unequaled for the ropes that "go down to the sea in ships."

Abaca, commercially known as manila hemp, is obtained from the sheathing leaf-stalks of the *Musa textilis,* a plant of the banana family and native to the Philippine Islands. More than 95 percent of the world's supply of the fiber comes from there and most of the remainder from the Netherlands Indies and British North Borneo. Our imports of abaca amounted to 57,900 long tons in 1940.

With our sole source of supply so far away American manufacturers began at the beginning of the war in 1939 to look around for a possible one nearer by. Panama seemed to be the most likely country in the Western Hemisphere in which abaca might be grown commercially, so production was started there in 1940. After Pearl Harbor it was decided to increase the first plantings—2,000 acres—ten fold. The fiber will be supplied to the government at cost for the duration. However, the plant does not yield satisfactory fiber in less than three years from the time of planting so demands cannot be met from this source for some time.

Manila hemp is, therefore, one material of which we may have a serious shortage unless a stock pile of considerable extent has been accumulated. No figures are available on this subject, but we can rest assured that the Navy Department has prepared for the present contingency.

In some cases, steel wires and cables could substitute for manila hemp, and for heavy duty it might even be possible to use paper cordage or a shrunken flax fiber as a core around which wire would be wound. If our manila hemp supplies become dangerously low before the Islands are once more free to export to us, some other fiber will have to do for all but the most essential uses.

Sisal

In an emergency sisal, though not quite as strong as manila hemp, could replace it even for heavy duty. Coming next to abaca in tensile strength, it is generally used for binding-twine.

Both *Agave sisalana,* which yields the true sisal, and its relative, *Agave fourcroydes,* yielding henequen are natives of Mexico. The two plants originated in Yucatan, where they still flourish. Late in the nineteenth century, sisal was introduced by the Dutch and British into their colonies of Java, Tanganyika and Kenya, and has become a leading citizen, as it were, of those far-off lands.

Not without reason did the planters of Java and East Africa choose sisal rather than henequen, for sisal is by far the stronger fiber of the two and makes a better twine or rope.

A very large percentage of the world's supply of sisal has come from those Dutch and British colonies, though small quantities are grown in Cuba and Haiti, and Mexico ships large amounts of both henequen and sisal.

We imported about 300,000,000 pounds in 1938. And war needs have greatly increased our requirements. Moreover if our supplies of manila hemp should become exhausted sisal would be still more in demand. The Army is already using a rope that is half sisal, half manila, and is 80 percent as strong as pure manila hemp.

It is fortunate, therefore, that some sisal is already grown in Latin America, and a much larger crop could certainly be harvested in an emergency. A shortage of binding-twine for civilian use is, however, a definite possibility. Henequen will undoubtedly be used to a large extent since so much more of it is available to us than the stronger sisal. And even istle, akin to the century plant and to henequen will probably be used for other things than cordage, brush bristles and upholstery as is now the case. Even yucca, which abounds in the desert Southwest, may be pressed into service for rope and cordage purposes.

Unmanufactured Jute: United States Imports for Consumption, by Principal Sources, in Specified Years, 1929 to 1940

COUNTRY	1929	1932	1936	1937	1938	1939	1940 [a]
			QUANTITY (LONG TONS)				
British India (including Burma)	56,765	26,499	62,860	91,120	34,508	34,578	45,517
Netherlands Indies	—	—	—	4	112	715	1
United Kingdom	109	1,352	1,906	688	—	—	—
China	156	125	90	124	31	—	—
All other	319	—	—	25	10	—	29
Total imports	57,349	27,976	64,856	91,961	34,661	35,293	45,547

[a] Preliminary.
SOURCE: Compiled from official statistics of the U. S. Department of Commerce.

Jute: Production in Principal Producing Countries of the World, in Specified Years, 1929 to 1938

COUNTRY	1929	1932	1936	1937	1938
			(IN LONG TONS)		
British India	1,845,516	1,262,822	1,716,241	1,545,680	1,191,172
Nepal [a]	11,348	8,681	9,566	9,812	8,297
Formosa	3,679	4,527	8,858	—	—
Japan	875	1,083	1,181	1,181	—
Indo-China	589	98	393	197	—
Iran [b]	—	1,378	3,740	—	—
All other	23	99	—	8,956	10,531
World total	1,850,682	1,268,629	1,726,673	1,556,014	1,201,703

[a] Exports of Nepal according to the statistics of imports into India across the land frontier. Not included in the total.
[b] Not included in total.
SOURCE: International Yearbook of Agriculture.

Henequen and Sisal: Exports from Principal Exporting Countries of Latin America and of the World, in Specified Years, 1929 to 1938

COUNTRY	1929	1932	1936	1937	1938
	QUANTITY (LONG TONS)				
Latin America:					
Mexico	255,147	301,356	159,128	158,264	117,710
Cuba	7,008	3,962	12,478	14,308	11,517
Haiti	106	6,662	12,500	13,675	15,924
El Salvador	2,205	1,186	2,262	2,368	a
Panama	—	—	258	143	a
All other	60	2	—	1,493[b]	1
Total Latin American countries	264,526	313,168	186,626	185,251	145,152[c]
Other countries:					
British East Africa	135,269	170,094	260,570	272,158	293,600
Netherlands Indies [d]	27,375	36,651	54,193	58,417	63,096
Portuguese East Africa	19,520	29,118	44,381	48,252	47,941
Angola (Portuguese West Africa)	—	3,179	10,818	11,023	a
French West Africa	1,687	4,495	8,847	9,674	9,850
Madagascar	926	1,184	5,459	5,814	5,439
Nyasaland	2,687	—	1,032	1,969	293
British West Indies	2,401	179	3,490	1,691	a
All other	597	624	966	2,115	a
World total	454,988	558,692	576,382	596,364	420,119[c]
	PERCENT OF WORLD TOTAL				
Latin America	58.1	56.1	32.4	31.1	34.6

[a] Not available.   [b] Includes Argentine exports of 705,000 pounds.
[c] Total incomplete.   [d] Production. Exports not available.
SOURCE: De Landbouwexportgewassen van Nederlandsch Indie. Converted to United States weights by applying the following factor: 1 metric ton = 2,204.6 pounds.

Abaca (Manila Hemp), Unmanufactured: United States Imports for Consumption, by Principal Sources, in Specified Years, 1929 to 1940

COUNTRY	1929	1932	1936	1937	1938	1939	1940 [a]
	QUANTITY (LONG TONS)						
Latin America	1	—	1	308	—	—	57
Other countries:							
Philippines	71,327	25,552	38,173	42,696	26,806	45,212	56,749
Netherlands Indies	408	40	809	698	577	720	2,053
United Kingdom	70	61	20	—	—	—	—
All other	384	6	24	—	—	—	5
Total imports	72,190	25,659	39,027	43,702	27,383	45,932	57,864

[a] Preliminary.
SOURCE: Compiled from official statistics of the U. S. Department of Commerce.

Abaca (Manila Hemp) : Production in Principal Producing Countries,
in Specified Years, 1929 to 1938 [a]

COUNTRY	1929	1932	1936	1937	1938
			(IN LONG TONS)		
Philippines	210,027	128,339	191,918	197,430	143,385[b]
Netherlands Indies	220	226	236	295	236

[a] Small quantities of manila hemp are also produced in British North Borneo; production statistics, however, are not available.

[b] Official statistics of the Philippines.

SOURCE: Compiled from the International Yearbook of Agricultural Statistics and from De Landbouwexportgewassen van Nederlandsch Indie.

PART II

Latin America

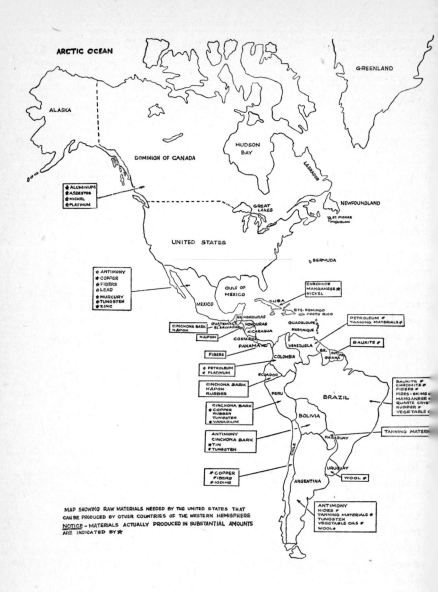

ARCTIC OCEAN

GREENLAND

ALASKA

DOMINION OF CANADA

HUDSON BAY

LABRADOR

NEWFOUNDLAND

★ ALUMINUM
★ ASBESTOS
★ NICKEL
★ PLATINUM

GREAT LAKES

ST. PIERRE MIQUELON

UNITED STATES

BERMUDA

★ ANTIMONY
★ COPPER
★ FIBERS
★ LEAD
★ MURCURY
★ TUNGSTEN
★ ZINC

GULF OF MEXICO

CHROMITE
MANGANESE ★
NICKEL

MEXICO

CUBA

STO. DOMINGO
PORTO RICO

PETROLEUM ★
TANNING MATERIALS ★

CINCHONA BARK
KAPOK

HONDURAS
GUATEMALA
EL SALVADOR
NICARAGUA

GUADELOUPE

MARTINIQUE

KAPOK

COSTA RICA

BAUXITE ★

FIBERS

PANAMA

VENEZUELA

BR.
GUIANA

COLOMBIA

★ PETROLEUM
★ PLATINUM

ECUADOR

CINCHONA BARK
KAPOK
RUBBER

PERU

BRAZIL

BAUXITE ★
CHROMITE ★
FIBERS ★
HIDES-SKINS ★
MANGANESE ★
QUARTZ CRYST ★
RUBBER ★
VEGETABLE O

CINCHONA BARK
★ COPPER
★ RUBBER
★ TUNGSTEN
★ VANADIUM

BOLIVIA

TANNING MATER

ANTIMONY
CINCHONA BARK
★ TIN
★ TUNGSTEN

PARAGUAY

CHILE

★ COPPER
★ FIBERS
★ IODINE

URUGUAY

WOOL ★

ARGENTINA

ANTIMONY
HIDES ★
TANNING MATERIALS ★
TUNGSTEN
VEGETABLE OILS ★
WOOL ★

MAP SHOWING RAW MATERIALS NEEDED BY THE UNITED STATES THAT
CAN BE PRODUCED BY OTHER COUNTRIES OF THE WESTERN HEMISPHERE
NOTICE - MATERIALS ACTUALLY PRODUCED IN SUBSTANTIAL AMOUNTS
ARE INDICATED BY ★

[7]

Our Southern Neighbors

Latin America

LATIN AMERICA has been frequently mentioned in these pages as a potential source of minerals and other products normally imported into this country from those parts of the world that are every day becoming more and more inaccessible. It might be well, therefore, to review the importance of the various countries to the south of us as regards their natural wealth and the possibilities of our receiving supplies from them.

Of considerable significance is the American capital invested south of the Rio Grande. We have a much larger investment there than many people realize. American commercial interests own a large share of the copper mines of Peru and Chile, and the vanadium deposits of Peru. A good percentage of Bolivian tin, of Chilean and Brazilian iron ore, and the manganese and chromite deposits of Brazil are controlled by American capital. And this is true of Venezuelan oil and the bauxite of Dutch Guiana.

Covering an area more than twice as large as that of the continental United States, Latin America is composed of twenty independent republics, of which half are on the southern continent. As each of these nations has its own economic situation, trade problems, resources, topography and climate, it is obviously impossible to study all of Latin America as a whole.

There are certain of the countries, however, which may be grouped together as having many common characteristics. The three Island Republics in the Caribbean, for instance, (Cuba, Haiti and the Dominican Republic); the six Central American countries; northern

South America (Colombia, Venezuela and Brazil); the west coast of
South America (Ecuador, Peru, Bolivia and Chile), the southeastern
countries (Argentina, Uruguay and Paraguay). Mexico must be put
in a class by itself because of its close proximity to the United States.
And for purposes of this study two small possessions of European
powers are included, British and Dutch Guiana.

Mexico

Mexico, fortunately, is blessed with large and varied mineral resources, which include several of the materials we need most for
national defense. There are, for instance, deposits of antimony,
tungsten and mercury in that country which may prove invaluable to
us in case of acute shortage. In 1940 we imported from Mexico 27,525
short tons of antimony ore and some metal, tungsten ore with a
tungsten content of 114,000 pounds and there seems to be little doubt
that these amounts could be increased.

Antimony is the most abundant of these strategic minerals in
Mexico. Nearly 65 percent of our imports of this metal in 1940 came
from that country. There are three sources of Mexican antimony: ores
from several localities, metal and alloys from lead ores smelted at
Monterrey, and mercury-antimony ores of the Huitzuco district in
Guerrero. A large part of the straight ores is exported to the Texas
Mining and Smelting Company plant at Laredo, Texas, while con-
centrates from the Huitzuco district go to the Menardi plant near
Los Angeles, where both mercury and antimony are recovered.

The tungsten deposits in Mexico are fairly small and that country
produced only 112 metric tons of concentrates containing 60 percent
wolframite in 1940.

In the case of mercury, however, Mexico, for years a large producer,
is our most promising potential source of supplies.

Output for 1940 in that country amounted to 11,653 flasks as compared to 7376 in 1939 and further increases can be expected.

The largest contribution to our war effort, so far, from our next
door neighbor has been in the form of copper. It hardly seems possible
that we who produce such tremendous quantities of that material—
35% of the total world output in 1940—should have needed as much
as 983,000,000 pounds from other countries that year. That is just how

much copper we imported, however, and 87,000,000 of those pounds came from Mexico.

Lead and zinc, too, are sorely needed for our arms program, in spite of our large domestic production; and Mexico is supplying us with some of these two metals—1,804 short tons of lead, 93,789 short tons of zinc ores in 1940.

Besides the mineral wealth of Mexico, the tropical climate of parts of the country offers distinct advantages from our point of view, since certain commodities can be produced there which cannot be grown within our own borders.

Sisal is one of these. This fiber, which may be needed to replace the manila hemp we may be unable to import for some time from the Philippines, can be obtained in Mexico. It would not be nearly as satisfactory as manila hemp, of course, especially as Mexican sisal is mixed with henequen, and not even pure sisal is as strong as abaca. Nevertheless, as we grow no fibers on a commercial scale in our own country, we would welcome this Mexican material which somehow could be used to make marine cordage.

Of real significance to this country is the Mexican guayule shrub from which crude rubber is obtained. American companies control several thousand acres of these plants near Torreon, which account for the total rubber production of the country, amounting to 3,000 long tons in 1938.

Since guayule rubber contains a large percentage of resin, in its pure state it can be used only for the making of rubberized fabrics; de-resined, it compares favorably with other types of crude rubber.

This means that an increase in the plantings of guayule shrubs and the harvesting of those that now grow wild in Mexico would add considerably to our supply of crude rubber. True, guayule rubber will have to be de-resined, but that will be the least of our worries now that we really face a rubber shortage.

Central American Countries

While bananas, coffee and cacao are the chief exports of these countries, and none of them is producing on a large commercial scale any raw materials essential to our defense efforts, they are the potential source of several of these commodities.

Guatemala, for instance, is already shipping to us some mica split-

tings and chromite; and in 1940 for the first time a small amount—
135,000 pounds—of cinchona bark was imported from that country.
This was equal—in quinine content—to only 33,750 pounds of Java
bark, so it amounted to less than 1 percent of our total imports of
cinchona bark for that year; but any cinchona bark at all from a source
nearby is of interest to the United States.

Kapok is another tropical product which is being developed in both
Guatemala and El Salvador, but fiber from these trees will not be
available before 1947 or 1948.

In Costa Rica there are plantings of rubber trees which some years
from now may prove of great value to the United States; and the
same is true of the increased plantings of manila hemp in Panama. The
latter do not yield satisfactory fiber in less than three years from the
time of planting; rubber trees require seven years to come into
bearing.

Obviously, Central America is not going to be able to help us very
much in the immediate emergency. These countries are of more interest to us from a long-range point of view.

The Island Republics

We are apt to think of Cuba, Haiti and the Dominican Republic
as solely sugar and tobacco producing countries, and it is true that
these, with a little coffee, are the principal products exported by all
three of them. Cuba, however, happens to be rich in certain minerals
of great significance for us at this time. Its deposits of manganese and
chromite and nickel are low-grade, it is true, but so extensive that at
wartime prices they can be profitably exploited.

The manganese is controlled chiefly by the Cuban American Manganese Corporation which was established in 1930 and has a present
refining capacity of 130,000 long tons of ferro-grade ore a year and a
potential emergency capacity of 300,000 tons by merely placing the
present plant on a 24-hour basis. The laying of additional trackage to
other holdings and the construction of a larger refinery may make it
possible to provide for a large part of the civilian and military needs
of our steel industry.

Cuba furnished 130,646 of the total 1,254,674 long tons of foreign
manganese ore used in the manufacture of ferromanganese in the

United States in 1940, all mined in the Province of Oriente and most of it by the Cuban American Manganese Corporation.

As for chromite, an American controlled company produced 52,789 metric tons in 1940, all of which were exported to this country, amounting to about 10 percent of our total imports of chromite. The extent of reserves is not known, but they are apparently quite large, so that Cuba could probably send us considerably more chromite. The ores from that country have a low content of chromic oxide and are principally used in the refractory industry.

The copper production of Cuba is also of significance to us today— in 1940 we imported 23,000,000 pounds from that country.

Work has been started on a large plant to recover nickel from low grade ores. The United States government has advanced $20,000,000 for this project.

[8]

Northern South America

HERE again cacao and coffee are among the principal exports, but in the case of each of these three republics at least one other product is of major importance. Venezuela is one of the world's largest producers of petroleum, which accounts for over 80 percent of that country's total exports. Brazil ships large amounts of cotton. Colombia, besides being the world's chief source of emeralds, produces large quantities of petroleum, platinum and gold.

Colombia

It is Colombia's platinum, of course, that is of major interest to us. That country and Canada now supply a large share of our imports of this metal and could probably meet most of our demands if we were forced to depend solely on them.

The usual and widespread deposits of platinum in Colombia are to be found in gold placers. Most of them were undeveloped before the last World War when our pressing need for the metal stimulated production. So great, indeed, was our demand for platinum at that time, so profitable its sale, that the very streets and sidewalks of one old mining town, Quibrido, were torn up to recover the platinum dust beneath them.

Since then this precious metal has been constantly produced in Colombia, and additional deposits have been discovered. One company alone produced 24,294 ounces in 1940. Our total imports from Colombia for that year were 34,011 ounces.

Venezuela

The Aruba refinery in the Dutch West Indies which has figured so largely in the headlines at various times since our entry into the war depends mainly upon Venezuelan oil for its operations and much of that oil is needed for the fighting ships of the United Nations. In other words petroleum from this South American country which is one of the largest producers in the world is vital to the war effort of the anti-Axis powers.

Venezuela also sends us considerable supplies of a tanning material necessary for our leather industry.

The Guianas

British and Dutch Guiana are extremely important to us right now because of their bauxite deposits, from which comes a large percentage of the raw material of the aluminum produced in this country and Canada.

In both colonies a great deal of activity has been going on lately. For instance, the new bauxite crushing and drying plant of the Surinamsche Bauxite Maatschappij at Paranam (Alcoa subsidiary) began operations February 15, 1941. This plant takes care of ore from newly developed mines at Topibo in the Para Creek district and has a capacity of 150 tons of dried bauxite an hour, or fifty tons more than can be produced at the older plant belonging to the same company at Moengo Hill.

Another recent development in Surinam is the new plant being constructed on the Surinam River near Paranam by the N. V. Billiton Maatschappij to treat bauxite from the Para Creek district.

As for British Guiana, it is estimated that in 1941 the Demerara Bauxite Company, Ltd., exported over 600,000 tons of bauxite to Canada, the United Kingdom and the United States. Also, it is reported that the Berbice Company, Ltd., is building a plant in this colony to process ore from its 4,000 acre concession.

Known resources in these small countries indicate that the region can continue to produce at the present rate (of about 1,000,000 tons a year) for thirty to forty years, and there are undoubtedly additional unexplored reserves of bauxite.

Water transport from the Guianas is cheap, and there seems to be no reason why we should not be able to continue importing their bauxite as usual, or even to a much larger extent once the submarine menace has been abolished.

Brazil

It is a curious—and unhappy—coincidence that Colombia, most accessible for us of all South American countries, having an extensive frontage on both the Caribbean Sea and the Pacific Ocean, produces but one of the materials essential to our national defense, while Brazil, the most vulnerable of them all to attack from Europe, is rich in several of the minerals we need.

All our quartz crystal, for instance, comes from Brazil and our entire communication system would be impaired without an adequate supply of those tiny oscillating discs which determine radio frequency. In fact, the accuracy of our fighting planes and the safety of our fliers depend on these totally unadvertised products of Brazil.

That is why radio manufacturers in this country send their own buyers to Brazil or have established purchasing agents there. Supplies of quartz crystal with the proper piezoelectrical qualities are far too important to be entrusted to general exporters.

Also significant to the United States are the high-grade bauxite deposits at Pocos de Caldas, where there is cheap and adequate labor. Most of these mines are owned by the Companhia Geral de Minas which contracted to supply the Reynolds Metals Company with 100,-000 metric tons of aluminum-grade bauxite in 1941 and 1942. Formerly the Companhia Geral mined and processed ore chiefly for shipment to São Paulo and Buenos Aires for the manufacture of aluminum sulfate.

There is plenty of bauxite in Brazil, but (and this is true throughout most of South America) not nearly enough transportation facilities. The railroad running from the Pocos de Caldas mines, for instance, to the nearest port, owns only enough cars to haul from 500 to 1,000 tons a month; and to ship economically to the United States at least 7,000 tons must be sent at a time.

Bauxite is not the only mineral tantalizingly plentiful in the hinterland of Brazil. That country has the largest deposits of chromite in South America. Production has never exceeded a few thousand tons a year (4,572 metric tons exported in 1940), but it is believed that mine development, improved transport facilities and favorable prices could bring about an annual output of as much as 100,000 tons.

Production of manganese in Brazil has been increasing. In 1940 exports totaled 217,342 metric tons (compared with 192,077 tons in 1939), nearly all of which came to the United States. Stocks on hand in Rio de Janeiro on December 31, 1940, were 68,212 metric tons.

Warren Lee Pierson, President of the United States Export-Import Bank, on his return from South America in May, 1941, reported that Brazil could provide still more manganese than was then the case; though their 1941 output was already estimated to be double that of 1940. Mr. Pierson also reported that their output of ferro-nickel could be considerably increased.

As a matter of fact, the only deposits of nickel ores in Brazil which have attracted attention in recent years are those at Luramento in the State of Minas Geraes, and those near São José de Locatins, in the State of Goiás. Only the former have been worked recently; they yield an ore, consisting largely of garnierite, which is treated in an electric furnace to produce ferro-nickel containing about 20 percent nickel. Reserves of this ore have been estimated at 4,000,000 to 10,000-000 metric tons of 1 to 4 percent nickel and the mine has a direct railroad connection with Rio de Janeiro, 176 miles away.

Transportation connections to the São José de Locatins deposits are less favorable; the nearest railroad is over 200 miles away and fuel for treating the ore is not to be found within a reasonable distance. Nevertheless, the deposits have been worked at various times—once as late as 1935, by the Empreza Commercial de Goiás, S. A., for shipments to Germany, and in 1939 the nickel mines and rights of this company were reported to have been purchased by a Japanese concern, but as far as we know no shipments have been made.

Mica (of which 1,117 metric tons were exported in 1940), industrial diamonds, zirconium, titanium and some other minerals are also abundant in Brazil and until recently lively competition between the representatives of various nations was going on down in Rio to obtain the limited supplies of these materials that are available for shipping.

Most of this wealth is still in the ground. Lack of transportation facilities is only one stumbling-block in the way of the exploitation of that country's natural resources. Another fundamental weakness is the absence of commercially exploitable deposits of oil, while those of coal are still undeveloped, making the cost of fuel for both transportation and industrial effort extremely high. Labor, too, is a consideration, as is the question of uncertain property titles.

We are interested in more than minerals in Brazil, however. Hides and skins from that country may become increasingly important. Rubber is already a matter of vital concern and the homeland of the *hevea brasiliensis* is of particular interest to us right now—wild rubber trees grow there in abundance—just such trees as those from which the precious seeds were taken to Java long ago. Until 1912, it will be remembered, a very large proportion of the total world production came from these uncultivated forests. With the advent of the improved Far East plantation rubber, the output of the production in Brazil began to decline rapidly. Even under the stimulus of our pressing need and consequent willingness to pay a good price, it is doubtful that Brazil right now could supply us with as much as 50 to 75,000 tons of wild rubber; all of South America produced but 49,000 tons in 1912, their peak year. Some years ago the Ford Motor Company started some large rubber plantations in Brazil. Unfortunately, however, most of these cultivated trees have not yet reached the bearing stage. They will eventually add a large amount to Brazil's output of rubber but for the immediate emergency they will make no appreciable difference. And kapok trees grow wild in Brazil, as they do in several other Latin American countries. The fiber is not usually harvested to the extent that will be profitable at war prices.

Other fibers grown in Brazil could, in a pinch be used in place of manila hemp for marine cordage. They are not now grown on a large commercial scale, but they constitute one more potential contribution of that rich country to our wartime and peacetime economy.

All this makes it obvious why, even excluding purely military reasons, German control of Dakar would be extremely unpleasant for the United States. From Dakar to Pernambuco is only about 1800 miles and should an enemy power get a foothold in Brazil we would lose a most valuable potential source of essential supplies.

[9]

West Coast Countries

THE ECONOMIES of Bolivia, Peru and Chile are all dominated by the production of minerals, chiefly for export. Bolivian tin, Peruvian petroleum, vanadium and copper, Chilean copper and nitrates, are not only the principal products of these countries but account for a large percentage of their total export tonnage.

These are not the only exports from the west coast of South America, however. Chile ships large quantities of wool, meats and vegetables, Peru a considerable amount of long-staple cotton, sugar, wool and other fine animal hair, while Ecuador is a large exporter of cacao and other agricultural products including the so called Panama hats.

Several of the minerals and agricultural products which we need the most from the western republics of South America do not now appear large among their export figures; but they may one day prove bonanzas for them and life-savers for us.

Ecuador

Smallest of the west coast republics, Ecuador differs from the others in being principally an agricultural country, and its products in which we are most interested are all of that nature. Many of them are decidedly strategic, coming normally from the Far East, and their presence in Ecuador makes that country extremely important for us today.

Kapok is being shipped from there in fairly large quantities (33 long tons in 1929, 421 long tons in 1936 and 328 long tons in 1937) and there is no reason why these amounts should not be considerably increased. It has not been profitable up to this point to harvest all

167

the fiber; but if the United States should require large amounts of kapok, the wild trees of Ecuador could be made to yield several times their present crop.

Also steadily rising are our imports of rubber from Ecuador; during 1940 they increased by 1,500,000 pounds—to a total of over 3,000,000 pounds. All of this came from wild trees and is not comparable in quality to rubber from the plantations of Malaya and Java; but it is rubber, and it can be used to equal advantage. Moreover, the amount of rubber shipped from Ecuador will probably be increased still further under the stimulus of war prices.

Like kapok and rubber, the cinchona tree grows wild in Ecuador. The bark is much lower in quinine content than that from the plantations of the Far East, and only about 160,000 pounds are normally exported from Ecuador in a year. Even this small amount might mean a great deal, however; and more of the bark will undoubtedly be collected and shipped as our growing needs boost prices.

There is one product, from Ecuador, balata wood, not mentioned on the list of strategic and critical materials, but which is being widely used at present to replace some of the light metals necessary for plane construction.

Peru

The land of the llama contains the largest vanadium mine in the world, responsible for a large percentage of the world's supply of that metal. This mine, situated in Minasagra, produced 23 percent more in 1940 than in 1939.

Peru also contains deposits of tungsten which, properly exploited, might help fill our war needs for that metal.

Still more interesting, however, are the developments going on in the production of rubber. We may be in much more pressing need of rubber than of any of the minerals and it is very heartening to realize that wild trees growing in Peru could be tapped for our use. Indians are already being sent, under expert supervision, into stands of these trees to gain experience in tapping. Should we have to use the wild rubber, uneconomic at normal prices for rubber, these men could bring it in.

Cultivation of rubber trees is also going on. Early in 1941 American experts joined with Peruvian agriculturists in the rehabilitation of an abandoned rubber plantation at Oramina; they have been testing rubber production there under commercial conditions and training Peruvian laborers in plantation operations. There is also an experimental station at Tingo Maria, which is exchanging seeds with experimental stations in other parts of the world.

The cinchona tree is another native of Peru and about 200,000 pounds of the bark is annually exported from that country. These Peruvian trees may become very valuable to us, and their yield might possibly be increased.

Of immediate value to the United States are Peruvian copper, zinc and lead. Like vanadium, these three materials, as mentioned above, are now needed in such great quantities that imports from Latin America are now of tremendous importance. Consequently, the 84,000,000 pounds of copper, 18,383 short tons of lead and about 17,000 tons of zinc received from Peru in 1940 were all welcome additions to our stocks.

Bolivia

Tin from Bolivia is already playing an important role in our defense efforts. With our usual source of supply now inaccessible, we are only too glad to see large shipments from South America of this metal so vital to armament manufacture.

Bolivia is the second largest tin producer in the world, exporting about 37,923 long tons in 1940, most of it from the Patino mines.

A large percentage of the crude metal has always gone to England, where it was smelted. Now, our Government has made a five-year contract with Bolivian producers to furnish us with 18,000 tons of tin a year, and at the close of 1940 20,000 tons of Bolivian ore were reported to be in Chilean and Peruvian ports awaiting shipment, of which a large share was destined for smelting in this country. Though the Patino groups are not participants in this ore contract, they have indicated an interest in plans for tin smelting in the United States.

The United States has also been negotiating with Bolivia for supplies of antimony (of which our imports from Bolivia were double in 1940 what they were in 1939) and for tungsten. We understand that in June 1941 the Bolivian Government was ready to prohibit the sale of wolfram to any country but our own. This means a good deal as wolfram is the principal Bolivian tungsten ore and that country is not only the largest tungsten producer in South America but is a close competitor of the United States, Portugal and Burma.

Four companies furnish about half of the total exports of Bolivian tungsten: International Mining Company (W. R. Grace & Company), Cia. Aramayo Minas de Bolivia, Bolivian Tin and Tungsten Mines Corporation, and Sociedad Empresa de Estano Araca. Their production will in all probability be expanded, as comprehensive mine-development work has been going on and modern mills installed.

As for the small companies that produce the other half of Bolivian tungsten, they not only mine the ore by hand but also use the old hand mills. Most of their output is purchased by the Banco Minero de Bolivia, the Government ore-buying agency.

While Bolivia's copper production in no way compares with that of Chile, Mexico, or Peru, 2,000,000 pounds of Bolivian copper were received in this country in 1940—and right now every pound of copper counts.

Bolivia also sent us relatively small amounts of zinc and lead ores.

Bolivia, like several of her neighbors, is going through a difficult period of adjustment due to the war. The country's economy, geared for many years to that of Britain, who took all the tin, cannot so easily be synchronized with that of the United States, now purchaser of half of that tin, half of the antimony and most of the tungsten and lead produced in Bolivia.

Chile

Chile, which in the First World War was tremendously important to us as the only source of the nitrates essential for explosives, is today in the limelight because of iodine, a by-product of those nitrates. Nitrate can now be made from the air, but no one has yet found a way to make artificial iodine.

We are producing iodine in large quantities from the brine of oil wells, and this source could probably be sufficient to supply all our war needs. Even so, control of the Chilean iodine production (through the Guggenheim interests, which control the two modern nitrate plants, Maria Elena and Pedro de Valdivia) is an "ace in the hole."

But Chilean copper is at least as necessary to us right now as iodine. This non-"strategic" but badly needed metal is mined in tremendous quantities in Chile—352,439 metric tons in 1940—of which 316,936 tons came to the United States.

We also imported 6,271 short tons of lead from that country in 1940 and this is another metal vitally important to the war effort and not now produced in sufficient quantity at home.

Chilean hemp is another product of significance today. This is not manila hemp but a strong fiber used for ropes. Production for 1938 was 5,100 long tons of unmanufactured hemp. This would indicate that Chile could help take care of our needs.

[10]

Southeastern Countries

URUGUAY, Paraguay and Argentina are largely dependent on the production of pastoral and agricultural commodities. Meats, wool, hides and skins, wheat, corn and flax-seed—these are their principal exports, to which we must add quebracho extract for Paraguay and Argentina.

Uruguay and Paraguay

Smallest of the South American republics and the poorest in mineral resources, Uruguay and Paraguay have, ironically, the best transportation facilities on the continent. No region of Uruguay is far from the port of Montevideo; no part of Paraguay is out of touch with the Paraná River, which empties into the Rio de La Plata, on which the harbor of Buenos Aires is located.

Consequently, as long as our lines of communication hold, our supplies of Uruguayan wool and Paraguayan quebracho extract for the leather trade are assured.

Argentina

Both wool and quebracho extract are imported in considerable quantities from Argentina. In fact, these two products are among the few things we really need from that country, for either peacetime or wartime use, and quebracho extract is the only one for which we are Argentina's best customer, buying about 80,000,000 pounds a year.

Production of this important material, as stated before, is controlled by a British concern, the Forestal Land, Timber and Railway Company, which owns tremendous forests in the Chaco. Quebracho extract is not all that our leather manufacturers buy from Argentina, however: a large proportion of the 5,000,000 hides we normally import come from that country. We may not need their beef, but we do use plenty of their hides.

We take a smaller proportion of Argentine wool, but still our imports now amount to about 40,000,000 pounds a year and if we should have difficulty in securing the supplies now coming from Australia, our purchase from Argentina will undoubtedly be more than doubled.

While Argentina is not as rich in minerals as some of the other South American countries it does contain deposits of antimony, tin, tungsten, lead and zinc.

The output of antimony was 18 tons in 1937, 383 tons in 1938, and 210 tons in 1939, most of it from the Pabellon mine at an altitude of 14,500 feet in the Cerro Granadas, where the ore is hand-sorted, crushed, and concentrated by primitive methods.

Apparently the present tin output of Argentina (1,600 long tons in 1940) is about sufficient for domestic consumption and the main placer deposits that supply the country's ore smelter are nearing exhaustion, though the tailings might be reworked to give about half the present output.

Quite a different situation exists in that country with regard to tungsten, for Argentina has become increasingly important as a source of this metal and now ranks fifth or sixth among producers. Except for one small shipment to Sweden, all exports of tungsten ore during 1940 (about 1,400 short tons) were sent to the United States and Japan, and the latter took only 19 percent. According to an agreement signed in 1941, all the tungsten mined in Argentina will come to the United States for three years.

Argentina also produced about 50,000 metric tons of 53 percent zinc concentrates in 1940 and shipped us 6,723 short tons of that metal as well as 16,469 short tons of lead of which their total production was 30,300 tons.

To sum up, Latin America is already supplying us with considerable amounts of three materials,—copper, lead and zinc—essential to our war effort and now "critical" because we need imports to fill our armament requirements. As for those raw materials which were already classed as strategic and critical before the beginning of the war, the great majority of them are not now being produced on a scale large enough to take care of the immediate emergency. It will take several years to have rubber, cinchona and kapok plantations in production, and at least that long to build up the transportation facilities necessary to efficient exploitation of the great mineral wealth of the southern continent.

Nevertheless, the very fact that the minerals, rubber and other products usually obtained from the Orient can be procured within our own hemisphere is of immeasurable significance. It means that the Western Hemisphere can be entirely self-sufficient, that the two continents are by nature in many ways complementary.

PART III

Additional Materials

[11]

Copper, Lead and Zinc

THESE three metals are a perfect example of what the present war has done to the raw material situation in this country. All of them have been produced for so long in such great quantities in the United States that their presence on a list of strategic or critical materials would have been a joke as recently as January, 1940. Things were quite different, however, by June of that year. The lightning German invasion of Norway, the Low Countries and France had awakened the United States to the need for a defense program and had made it imperative that Britain receive large quantities of armaments as rapidly as possible.

To make these meant the production of unprecedented amounts of copper, lead and zinc, and it was not long before domestic mines were unable to keep pace with smelter capacity.

American producers needed foreign ores, and these were available in Mexico and South America. It was fortunate for all concerned because the very ores needed by the United States were lying idle in Latin American ports, their usual markets closed to them by the British blockade. Here was a classic example of the interdependence and mutual helpfulness of the countries of the Western Hemisphere.

Copper

Copper was being produced early in 1940 in much greater quantities than it could be sold; European markets had been closed and users at home did not take nearly enough to compensate for this loss. Six months later these same copper producers were having such a hard time to keep up with the demands of domestic fabricators that they actually welcomed an influx of the foreign metal usually kept out by the four percent tariff.

The electrolytic refineries responsible for most of our copper output, operated at 90 percent of capacity that year; and domestic production was not only 28 percent higher than in 1939 but was the sixth largest output in our history, exceeded only by the war years, 1916-1918, and the boom years '28 and '29.

But the 1,756,172,000 pounds produced by our mines was not enough, and for the first time since the tariff had been put on copper, our imports of that metal exceeded exports and were the highest on record. Chile, Canada and the Belgian Congo were the principal sources of these imports, some of which came also from Mexico, Peru, British South Africa, etc.

By September of that year, when it had become all too evident that domestic production of copper would not be enough to care for our defense needs and shipments of arms to Britain, the Metals Reserve Company began working on arrangements to assure our supplies of Latin-American copper.

The first Government contracts were signed on December 19, 1940, and amounted to 100,000 short tons—to come from Chile, Peru and Mexico. By April of 1941 contracts had been signed calling for 500,497 tons (from the same countries), and we are undoubtedly taking larger amounts by now.

One of the most significant features of the 1940 contracts was the fact that the Chilean Government assumed the right to suspend exports of copper to Japan when the metal was needed in the United States, and shipments to the Nipponese from Canada were suspended that year.

Japan had been our leading customer, too, up to that point and undoubtedly a large proportion of the shells now being fired on American troops in the East come out of cartridge cases made of American copper.

In this connection it is interesting to note just how much copper is consumed by only one variety of the thousands and thousands of guns being fired all over the world right now. Take, for instance, the .303 small arms cartridge, used quite extensively in aircraft machine-guns. One minute's full firing by a fighter plane with eight of these guns (that is 9,600 rounds) results in the expenditure of 240 pounds of copper in the cartridge cases spread over the countryside or the sea.

In bomber craft the loss of copper is not as great, for the bulk of the cartridge cases is recovered, since they fall within the bomber. Naval guns, land batteries, infantry rifles and machine-guns all scatter their shells, however, and most of them are shooting far more than 240 pounds of copper a minute.

This is one of the reasons why radios and refrigerators and automobiles cannot be manufactured right now and why new copper pipes for civilian use are out of the question. All the plumbing that might have been is being spread over the seven seas! Light and power lines, telephone and telegraph lines, will continue to be erected where needed, and the rest of the copper available will go into ammunition and ship-building.

Lead

The lead refineries of this country found themselves in 1940 in nearly as bad a situation as the copper producers; the output of domestic ore in spite of a decided increase was just not enough to take care of the needs of the defense program. Consequently a record quantity of lead was imported that year. In fact, the imports of pig lead were more than four times greater than they had ever been—even in the freak year of 1920.

Production of refined primary lead in 1940 amounted to 533,179 short tons, of which 433,065 short tons were made from domestic ores (12,098 short tons more than in 1939). Imports came to 100,114 short tons as compared with 63,068 short tons in 1939. A large part of these came from Mexico, Peru, Newfoundland, Argentina, Australia and South Africa.

The only important direct use for lead in armaments is ammunition, but this is enough to consume great quantities of the metal. Like copper, it is being scattered over various parts of the world in enormous amounts, since it is the principal ingredient of all light arms bullets.

And the uses for lead which have indirect importance to the arms program are many: storage batteries (these will soon be unavailable for civilians), bearing metals for motorized equipment, lead paints for military structures, chemical lead for the construction of explosive plants, tetraethyl lead for high-octane gas (another thing soon to be difficult for Mr. John Q. Public to secure).

Zinc

The story of zinc, like that of copper and lead, is one of abundant domestic supplies up until 1940, when suddenly even a 33 percent increase in smelter output was not sufficient to meet the demands for our own defense projects and British armament requirements. With all smelters working at capacity and additions being made as rapidly as possible it was necessary to import large amounts of foreign ores, since American mine output was increased by only 14 percent.

Again as in the case of copper and lead, the ores were available in South America and this country benefited by the fact that markets in Europe had been closed by the British blockade.

The Germans, by invading Norway, Holland and Belgium, gained control that summer of plants with a zinc reduction capacity which, added to that of the Reich, amounted to over one-third of the world total. What they did not gain, however, were corresponding sources of ore supply; the ore needed to keep these European smelters running at capacity had to be brought from South America or the East and the British blockade made this impossible. It is not known just how much zinc is now being produced in the Axis held countries but one thing is certain—that smelters which have always had to depend on imported ores cannot now be producing their full quota.

Our own smelting capacity has been growing fast. In October, 1940, the Bureau of Mines published a survey in which production for that year was estimated at 816,000 short tons, which was expected to be increased to 825,000 short tons in 1941, 956,000 short tons in 1942.

Domestic mine output was expected to reach 714,000 tons a year, or 216,000 tons less than would be needed for smelter capacity. More than 270,000 tons were estimated to be available from stocks in South America (Argentina, Bolivia, Peru) and Mexico, and shipments from these areas could be increased, it was believed, by more than 300,000 tons a year.

The problem has been to find enough shipping space to bring in this large amount of zinc ore. Consequently, domestic production has been stimulated even more than was planned and, so far as is known, our smelters are receiving enough ore to keep their production in line with our war needs.

Petroleum

ITS STRATEGIC IMPORTANCE IN THE UNITED STATES DEFENSE PROBLEM

by Harold J. Wasson

LIQUID FUEL—the driving force of modern war machines, whether used in the air, on the ground, the sea, or under the sea—is no less important than the machines themselves.

The military striking power of a nation, in a mechanical sense, thus can be measured accurately by its military and naval consumption of gasoline, fuel oil and diesel oil, the three principal products of petroleum. It can, in fact, be expressed more significantly by fuel consumption than in terms of equipment itself, since only when the equipment is in action is there any application of mechanized combatant force. When it is in action it is consuming fuel and lubricants which can be supplied in immediate abundance only by petroleum.

A simple illustration is cited:

An average two-motor bomber in flight consumes approximately two barrels of motor fuel an hour, or for a bomber year—that is, 8,760 hours—a total of 17,520 barrels, if operated continuously. For every bomber hour in the air there is probably at least twice as much consumption of motor fuel by auxiliary planes, escorts, pursuits, fighters, reconnaissance, trainers, supply trucks, etc. Thus one may express the military striking force represented by twenty-four hours of bomber flight a day for one year as the expenditure of three times 17,520 barrels, or in round numbers 50,000 barrels of motor fuel, either gasoline or diesel oil.

This figure is probably on the low side since an increasing proportion of bomber planes is equipped with four motors which consume approximately twice the amount of fuel taken as the base for this illustrative calculation. In any event it is evident that the maintenance of bomber striking power requires large fuel resources and in consequence a paramount problem of war effort is the procurement of the fuel required to maintain an air force of sufficient size to insure air supremacy. In the final analysis air supremacy means simply an over-

whelming excess of offensive air power, which if applied for a sufficient time, will demolish the enemy's munition supply sources and
thereby lay the foundation for the ultimate defeat of his field armies,
a final operation in which air power also plays a leading role. In
modern war the development of offensive striking power from air-
borne craft has progressed to a point where it has become the critical
determinant of victory or defeat.

Just what surplus of bomber striking power over that of the Axis
nations will be necessary to insure victory to ourselves and our allies
is a problem for the military leadership quite outside the scope of these
observations. As will be shown herein, however, the correct appraise-
ment of this problem is as much a derivative of fuel considerations as
it is of the respective industrial capacities for actually making planes
or of man power for their operational requirements.

On the basis of publicly announced construction plans it may be assumed that the United Nations are rapidly approaching, if they have
not already assembled, a front line fleet of 6,000 bombers. Assuming
that on the average over the course of a year a bomber will spend one-
sixth of the time in the air, a fleet of 6,000 bombers would expend
during a year of active campaigning the equivalent of 1,000 years of
the continuous 24 hour a day fuel consumption of one bomber. That
is, on the basis of 50,000 barrels of motor fuel for each front line
bomber, including auxiliary air force units, 1,000 times 50,000 barrels,
or 50,000,000 barrels, would be required during the year.

There is no implication that this particular estimate is accurate to
a close degree. It is presented in the belief, however, that it represents
the general order of magnitude of fuel consumption that would be
required over a year of active operations by an air force, the nucleus
of which is a fleet of 6,000 bombers.

As is shown clearly by the figures for world oil production given
at the end of this chapter, the United States alone could support many
such fleets, whereas it is doubtful if the Axis powers, on the basis of
their existing fuel resources, could support in the European war theatre
an air striking power that approaches this size; and that Japan, unless
successful in consolidating her control of Southwest Pacific and Burma
oil reserves could maintain but a small fraction of such air power
over a protracted period.

Emphasis has been given to the fuel requirements of air power
because it strikingly shows the enormous volume of liquid fuel that

will be needed for this absolutely essential requirement of victory in total war. Air power, of course, constitutes but one element of the complete war machine, and though it might be said that no modern war could be won without air dominance, it is equally true that no modern war could be won, at least in totality, by air power alone. Accordingly the fuel requirement for total victory goes far beyond the needs of the air force.

Mechanized combat ground equipment, and motorized vehicles which supply the war machine as a whole, also consume great quantities of fuel, and sea power on the scale maintained by the United Nations is probably a greater consumer of liquid fuel than all other elements of the armed forces combined.

Taken all together, the air, land, and marine consumption of liquid fuel in the world war now in progress is reaching unprecedented volumes, and the trend is rapidly upward as the myriads of new machines leave the factories and shipyards and take their places in the line of battle.

No precise overall figure can be given at this time for the probable oil consuming capacity of our own military and naval forces when the peak of their projected power is reached. It appears to the writer well within the realm of possibility that our forces alone will have mobilized by the early part of 1943 mechanized power—air, land and sea—that will be capable of consuming during a year's campaign, a volume of refined products that will be equivalent to some 400 million barrels of crude oil. Great Britain and Russia together may be prepared over the same period to expend another 250 million barrels of oil.

The annual production rate of Axis controlled fuel supply available to the European war theatre presently is of the order of 100 million barrels a year and, except by conquest of additional oil regions no great gain above this level seems probable over the next two years.

A large part, possibly half, of the American military oil will doubtless be expended in the Pacific war theatre where the enemy's fuel position as a result of conquest is relatively strong, but the amount actually used by United States combatant forces operating with Great Britain and Russia in Europe and Africa may be exceeding the Axis consumption month by month before the end of this year. The overall oil situation for at least the next few months will be preponderantly in favor of the United Nations.

Modern war is a race of power against power. To be sure, man power is basic, but it is the least scarce. The critical balance lies in those elements of industrial power required to build weapons and the fuel power essential to motivate them. Of all forces, man, industrial, and fuel, the great disparity in potential military might today between the two opposing groups of world powers lies in their respective liquid fuel resources. Their fuel supplies gauge the ceiling of their possible war efforts, their respective fuel ceilings establishing the measure of maximum military striking power attainable by a belligerent in the present world conflict, as they did in the last war, when, in the words of Winston Churchill, "the Allies floated to victory on a sea of oil."

It is not to be presumed, of course, that the potential military power of nations can be rated on the basis of comparative oil resources alone. Obviously, the fuel must be made accessible to front line consumption, which requirement involves formidable problems of transportation, distribution and storage, and the fuel consuming machines themselves, in endless number and variety, must be swarming over land and sea, and through the air.

However, presupposing that the time factor, which enters into every evaluation of military effort, is limited only by the amount necessary to attain the end sought, it is unquestionably within the power of the anti-Axis nations to provide the facilities that will be required to make oil products in practically any amount accessible to their war effort.

Thus, the combination of an incomparably more abundant supply of fuel, and the technological power to provide equipment and means for its use in vastly larger quantities than the aggressor nations can match with their present resources, is one of the greatest advantages, possibly the greatest, that the anti-Axis nations have on their side.

Seemingly the only possibility that the Axis powers can not be defeated ultimately—that is, in a long war—is dependent on their ability to augment their fuel supply by conquest in time to sustain the much heavier war effort that inevitably will be required of them as the mechanized attacking forces of the United Nations, unlimited by any considerations of fuel supply, continue their growth into the hitherto unimagined levels of strength which is now under way in this country and elsewhere throughout the anti-Axis world.

In the United States, military fuel, except for insignificant amounts used in the few coal burning auxiliary craft still in service, comes from petroleum, or crude oil, as it is commonly called. This is substantially true, likewise, in all other countries of the world, except in Germany, where the acute shortage of natural crude oil reserves within her own borders has led to the development of processes whereby "synthetic oils" are derived from coal.

Germany produces some crude oil and controls the output of oil wells in Rumania and Poland, together with the insignificant output of the rest of Europe, and from these manufactures gasoline, diesel oil, and other petroleum products, as is done in this country. But these are not enough, not nearly enough, for either the war economy or the peace economy of Europe, and in the absence of imports from enemy controlled oil reserves, over half of Germany's requirements in the war thus far, it is estimated, have been supplied by the synthetic fuels.

Japan produces a relatively very small amount of crude oil, but in recent years has been developing a synthetic industry that by this time may have reached substantial proportions. It is inconceivable, however, that Japan's fuel resources, always excepting the possibility that it is able to retain control of the East Indies reserves, can maintain more than a fraction of the mechanized forces—air, land and water—that we, given time, can bring into the conflict in the Pacific area.

Lubricating oils and greases used throughout the world, again excepting Germany and possibly Japan, are also products of crude oil. In Germany synthetic substitutes for petroleum lubricating products are of necessity obtained from coal by variations of the processes employed to produce motor fuels such as gasoline and diesel oil, and the heavier fuel oils used in most marine engines. The Germans, as is well known, have made great progress in providing substitutes for almost everything that nature has not supplied them in convenient abundance.

However, the problem of providing satisfactory lubricating oil supplies to their mechanized forces constitutes, it is believed, one of the most restrictive bottlenecks confronting the war effort of the Axis powers. The manufacture in volume synthetically of the highly specialized quality of lubricating oils demanded by modern high compression airplane motors, and the various grades required for such diverse land campaigns as those of torrid Africa and sub-zero Russia, may not be a technological impossibility, but there can be little doubt but that it presents formidable difficulties. These difficulties may even be the Fuehrer's Achilles heel, or perhaps one of the many vulnerable spots that time will reveal as his pre-war accumulation of strategic material stocks is consumed.

No attempt is made to minimize the magnitude of mechanized war effort expended thus far by the Germans, but the machines, particularly the air machines, in all probability have been lubricated in large part with imported oil that had been accumulated through the pre-war years. The unconsumed stocks of high quality lubricating oil remaining in Germany is conjectural, but the time inevitably will come, if it has not already arrived, when the various types of lubricating oil required by its complex war machine, if anything like maximum efficiency is to be attained, will be critically scarce in Germany.

In a broad sense, the importance of petroleum lies in the fact that it is the raw material from which motor and marine boiler fuels of highest quality, as well as lubricating products, can be derived most cheaply. Petroleum is not alone, however, in the field of liquid fuel since all of its products can be obtained from coal—as is now being done by both the Germans and Japanese. In future years this will be universal practice in all other countries, since the coal reserves of the world are practically unlimited, whereas the oil reserves of the world may be substantially depleted within a century, or at least within a brief period as compared to that required to exhaust the world's coal reserves.

These long term considerations are, of course, quite academic so far as the present problem of national defense and the contemporary war economy of the world at large are concerned.

Actually the immediate advantages of petroleum reserves to the nations which control them are very great. A nation restricted in large part to synthetic fuels cannot expand its production at anything like the rate possible in petroleum-rich countries. The former are at a tremendous disadvantage when the mechanical war equipment of these latter countries reaches a fuel consuming point beyond that which a country deficient in petroleum can equal.

Synthetic oil plants capable of competing with prolific oil fields require vast capital expenditures, and even if the money cost consideration were ignored, as it could be in a totalitarian state, the very magnitude of physical plant construction would impose a crushing load on the national war economy through absorption of labor and materials. But, above all, so much time would be required that, as an emergency defense measure, it could never cope with the volumes of available military fuel which quickly can be mobilized by nations controlling or having access to large reserves of petroleum, and the requisite refining facilities for its speedy conversion into usable products.

The present position of the United States with respect to immediately available petroleum reserves is incomparably stronger than that of any other country. This is clearly established by the fact that this country has produced more oil than the rest of the world combined for every year since oil became an important commodity.

Considering the military situation at the beginning of 1942 from the world viewpoint, the respective oil strengths of the opposing nations are shown in the table at the end of this chapter.

As will be observed from this table, the Axis was opposed at the first of the year 1942 by 94.5 percent of the world's oil productive capacity. As of the date at which this is written—May, 1942—the situation has changed in one theatre of the war in a manner that has brought about in that area a very unfavorable situation to the United Nations. The Japanese conquest of Sumatra, Borneo, Java and Burma, has brought under enemy control all of the oil resources lying within a very large fraction of the world's surface area. It is conjectural whether these resources will be immediately available to Japan, since extensive destruction of the oil field and refinery installations is presumed to have been accomplished by the defenders before capitulation. Nevertheless the ratio of anti-Axis to Axis controlled oil in this particular war theatre has become extremely adverse.

The overall world relationship, however, has not been greatly changed by the Japanese encroachments, for if Table I were to be revised by transference of the East Indies and Burma oil from the United Nations to the Axis, the totals would be changed only from 2,166,000,000 barrels and 126,000,000 barrels to 2,090,000,000 barrels and 202,000,000 barrels respectively, which still leaves the United Nations with a powerful advantage (91.2% against 8.8% of total), if no further inroads on their oil reserves are sustained.

The Japanese campaign is a most enlightening example of the major role that oil plays in the strategy of total world war. To exist as a world power nation Japan had to have abundant oil resources under its own domination; and in the direction of accomplishing this objective it has achieved a notable success in an incredibly short space of time.

This success in Japan's case is not conclusive, in the belief of the writer, since it is also true that oil alone cannot win a war without the industrial power plant to create the mechanisms for its use in volume comparable with that of its enemies. It is believed, therefore, that even with the handicap of necessitous long distance transportation of fuel to the front line in the Southwest Pacific area, that the vastly greater industrial capacity of the United States establishes a military power potential that will crush Japan in time. If a considerable time is required by Japan to rehabilitate the conquered oil fields, its position is precarious, notwithstanding its initial gains.

The dynamic impetus that the Pacific area reverses will give (it is presumed) to the development in our country of the now desperately needed long range air power capable of direct attack on Japan may prove to be even providential. That is, these humiliating defeats in the Pacific may shock the country into a realistic consciousness of the grim peril that actually does threaten, and thereby accelerate the creation of weapons indispensable to victory while there is yet time.

The critical threat to the dominant oil position of the United Nations is not the Japanese conquests in the Southwest Pacific area, but the menace of the German army to the Russian oil fields of the Caucasus, the control of which was in all probability the prime motivating incentive behind the Axis march against Russia on that memorable day in June, 1941. The pattern of world events for immeasurable decades of time hangs in the balance as this particular oil reserve either preserves its identity as a bulwark of strength for the United Nations or passes to the control of the Axis bloc and becomes an ominous military potential in hostile hands.

If the Axis campaign in Russia should be victorious, only a few months, possibly a year, would be required to organize the essential lines of supply that would be needed to place Germany in an impregnable position from a liquid fuel standpoint. With no fuel limitations on its war machine Germany would be enabled to extend its campaign southward from Russia toward the vast British controlled oil reserves of Iraq, Iran, Arabia and Egypt. Such a campaign would not be unopposed, to be sure, but the enormous fuel advantage the United Nations now possess would be offset by ample Russian oil in German hands. Moreover, the occupation of bases in southern Russia would enable Germany to attack the Middle and Near East oil fields from a new and strategically located front.

Heavy combined pressure on these vital oil areas from two directions —Russia on the north and Libya on the west, might create a tactical situation that would be seriously unfavorable considering the extreme length of the line of communications upon which the opposing Allied armies would have to depend.

These observations emphasize the critical importance of oil as a basic factor in the war situation, and also how a gain in oil at one point may implement the force required to gain more oil in a new region and thereby a gain of still more potential military strength.

Should the possibilities eventuate—the conquest of Russia followed by a thus greatly facilitated invasion of Iran, Iraq and Egypt—the military strength of the Axis would be immeasurably enhanced. Unlike the situation in the Southwest Pacific, Germany and subjugated Europe have very substantial industrial power even in comparison with the United States and Great Britain. The Axis in western Europe can, in consequence, make effective military use of every barrel of new oil that comes within its grasp. With the Axis controlling a substantial proportion of the world's oil resources, as would be the case if Russia, the Middle East and Near East countries should succumb, the defense of any part of this globe, save the Western Hemisphere, would become extremely difficult. Even here in the two American continents endowed as we are with almost unlimited industrial, fuel, and man power, our national existence would be gravely imperiled in a world wherein the forces of aggression dominated equal and in many cases greater elements of potential military power.

It seems fitting to emphasize again the vital role that oil plays in our defense, and how important it is to understand that *our defense* means defense of oil under control of our friends as much as it does the oil within our own national boundaries. As the writer has endeavored to show, oil is potential military power which in some respects is more critical in the world as now constituted than either man power or industrial power. Its transference from allies to enemies is in the nature of a military defeat to ourselves. More accurately perhaps, it should be characterized as the advance warning of a future attack that will inevitably be launched at us by the enemy as soon as he strengthens his fuel resources to the point that he estimates will enable him to defeat us.

The obvious truth of these considerations was grasped, presumably, by our Government many months before Pearl Harbor and may well have been a major incentive behind the all-out Lend-Lease program at a time when so many of our nationals were still following the phantom trail of isolationism toward a mirage that they envisioned as security.

History has yet to record whether or not the providential resistance of the Russians and consequent failure of Hitler to occupy the Caucasus oil fields in the winter of 1941-42 gained for the United Nations a time respite that will prove to have been the crucial turning point. It is crystal clear, however, that these Russian oil resources are still the most vulnerable citadel of the many which *must* be preserved if victory—not stalemate, but absolute victory—is to be the portion of the United Nations.

Successful defense of our own oil reserves, however, is only a partial formula for victory. The enemy's oil supply position in Europe still is precariously meager and steadily becomes less sufficient relative to the volume of military fuel being mobilized against him. It may be presumed, therefore, that in the battle for oil Hitler will have no monopoly on offensive action. The synthetic oil plants in Germany have had high ratings on the R.A.F.'s list of targets for a long time, and there is considerable basis for believing that the growth of the enemy's synthetic oil production is retarded, to say the least. Reference to the oil-production table will reveal the striking fact that Rumania supplies the Axis war machine with approximately 36,000,000 barrels of oil out of a total yearly supply of 100,000,000 barrels (including crude oil equivalent of synthetic products). This is another very vulnerable chink in the thin oil armor that admittedly has been strong enough so far, but that one day may be cracked with history-making repercussions in favor of our side.

Any appreciable restriction of Axis oil resources in the European theatre at this juncture might well be the turning point of the war.

In the foregoing pages the writer has attempted to sketch in broad outline the tremendous strategic importance of petroleum in a world at war, and how even our own security, distant as we are from the far flung battle fronts, is closely inter-related with the fortunes of war.

There is yet another side to this picture that also is of great importance to every citizen in the United States. We, in this country,

have accustomed ourselves to live in confident reliance on an unlimited supply of gasoline and other petroleum products. Thereby
the pattern of our existence has been influenced profoundly. Does war
mean that all this will be changed?

The impact of war on civilian consumption of oil products in this
country presents a situation unlike that prevailing with respect to
any of the other major strategic commodities. Shortage of oil for
civilian use is not caused by the huge war requirements. Gigantic as
our war effort will be, and it has been said above that it may reach a
level of annual fuel consumption several times greater than the
amount of oil that now can be produced in all Europe by the German-
Italian Axis partners over the course of a year, it constitutes no serious
strain on the hemisphere (hardly our own even) capacity to produce oil.

Domestic consumption of oil in the United States for the year
1941 (a year in which military use played a relatively small part) was
1,487,000,000 barrels. The capacity of our oil fields together with those
of Venezuela is such that this volume of production plus a super-
imposed war production load of even half a billion barrels a year
could be maintained for several years from known oil reserves. With
continued replenishment of known oil reserves by new oil field dis-
coveries at rates in line with past experience such output could be
maintained for at least a decade.

Any restriction of civilian oil products use will thus come from
other causes than shortage of oil itself. The two factors that will
tend to curtail civilian use of oil products (principally gasoline and
industrial fuel oil) are, for certain areas, a lack of marine transportation as more tankers are required for duty in the active war theatres.
For the country as a whole the practical stoppage of civilian tire replacement will, of course, reduce the possible miles of travel quite
irrespective of the gasoline supply, or lack of it.

The shortage of tanker transportation affects principally the
Atlantic Coast states, but so far as the critical requirements for oil
burner fuel are concerned in this area, they can and will be supplied
by railroad tank cars even if no coastwise tankers are running. To
do this, however, the tank car fleet will have little or no capacity
for gasoline movement as the winter of 1942-43 approaches, and a
gasoline scarcity in the north Atlantic Coast states, particularly, will
probably continue for several months into 1943. Eventually more rail-

Estimated World Oil Production in 1941
(MILLIONS OF BARRELS)

UNITED NATIONS CONTROLLED OIL

Western Hemisphere

United States	1404	
Canada	10	
Mexico	35	
Trinidad	21	
Venezuela	223	
Colombia	24	
Peru	13	
Ecuador	1	
Argentina	22	1753

Middle and Near East

Egypt	8	
Iran	78	
Iraq	10	
Bahrein Island	7	
Saudi Arabia	6	
British India	2	
Russia	226	337

Southwest Pacific

Burma	7	
Netherlands Indies	62	
Borneo	7	76
TOTAL (94.5% of World Total)		2166

road tank cars, a great increase in barge movement of oil products up
the Mississippi and eastward through various links of our inland
waterway systems and also up the Atlantic Coast through the coastal
canal system will combine to relieve the situation for gasoline. As
stated, the domestic fuel oil requirements of the area can be supplied
by existing facilities.

The interior regions of the United States will be little affected
except as the transference of railroad tank cars to the critical eastern
area may lead to moderate curtailment. Throughout the Central
States there are numerous refining centers which are connected by
pipelines to the oil fields of the Southwest. The supply of crude oil
for these areas thus need not be interrupted. The great bulk of the
refined products in these refining centers are distributed by motor
truck and this movement should continue normally.

Estimated World Oil Production in 1941: *Continued*
(MILLIONS OF BARRELS)

AXIS NATIONS CONTROLLED OIL
European Theatre

Roumania	36	
Germany	4	
Poland	3	
Austria	1	
Hungary	2	
Albania	1	
Miscellaneous	1	48

Pacific Theatre

Japan	3	
Sakhalin Island	5	8

Estimated Synthetic Oil (Equivalent)

Germany	50	
Japan	20	70
TOTAL (5.5% of World Total)		126

NOTE: The oil production figures shown above are round number approximations of esti-mate prepared and published by the Oil Weekly under date of January 26, 1942.

The figures for Axis synthetic oil equivalents are those of the author. These figures represent the volume of oil that would be required to produce the estimated volume of refined products presently being obtained directly from coal by synthetic processes. Accurate information on the synthetic production of refined products in Germany and Japan is not available, but based on reasonably accurate prewar figures the estimates presented above are believed to be liberal—that is in excess of the actual amounts.

In any event, the question of sacrifice that the exigencies of war may impose on our domestic oil consumption habits over the next few months, or even years, are trivial indeed in comparison with the protective contribution which our hemisphere oil reserve gives us in this historic moment of our greatest national danger.

Chemicals

Growth of the American chemical industry in two decades between World War I and World War II was so phenomenal as to arouse at once both the admiration and the extreme envy of a large part of the rest of the world. In twenty years a rather modest industry expanded vertically and horizontally to such an extent that its figures of production more than topped the combined output of any other three countries—a proud record and a notable achievement.

Under such unusual circumstances there was every reason for us to be supremely confident that the chemical industry could meet all the requirements of a national defense program or a war program, even one of tremendous magnitude, and yet at the same time provide with a minimum of inconvenience and curtailment the regular normal requirements of chemicals consumed in what is loosely termed "non-defense" industries. Of course, being geared to a peace economy and not a war economy we did thoroughly realize that in a few certain divisions, notably explosives, change-overs and plant expansions were inevitable; and this was looked upon as the price democracy must pay for daring to live side by side with totalitarianism.

But even before the tragic events of the Sunday morning of December 7, it had become all too self-evident that in certain divisions at least the chemical industry, despite its accomplishments, despite its size, was under-equipped and possibly under-manned to meet the wholly unexpected demands being placed upon it by Mars, the greatest of chemical consumers. And the end is not yet in sight. Indeed, we may just be stepping upon a dark and uninviting threshold with little appreciation or understanding of what may await us within the portals.

In the not far-distant past competent and well-qualified spokesmen of the chemical industry have with great and wholly understandable pride indulged in the pastime of informing the American lay public, through the medium of the printed word and the radio, about facts and figures best illustrating the expansion in chemical productive capacity. Now it is very apparent that editors, business executives and prominent technologists were totally unaware of the demands that would ultimately be made for American chemicals in the present death-struggle. Even a chemical industry with a productive capacity generally admitted to be equal to the combined capacity of the industries of England, Germany and France, could hardly be expected to meet immediately the wholly unexpected role of the "chemical arsenal of democracy."

Has American chemical management been guilty of a grave mistake in underestimating the chemical requirements of an all-out war program? The answer is very definitely No. And for the following reasons:

In the first place, the first year of the present struggle was popularly described as a "phony war." Looking backward we can recall quite vividly how practically everybody believed that the war on the Continent would be one of short duration. In these two beliefs the chemical manufacturer was no different from the layman on the street. How could the producer of chemicals be expected to foresee what no one else could foretell?

Have we any right, then, to criticize because chemical plant productive capacity was not expanded several years ago well beyond the point where there appeared to be any possible expectation of utilizing such capacity for peacetime needs? It is just a little more than a year ago that it became self-evident that the American chemical industry would be called upon to become the "chemical arsenal of democracy" and to assume the burden of supplementing England's chemical production as well as to supply the greatly enlarged chemical requirements of the Soviet, Chinese and South American markets.

This was a tremendous task to assume because in normal times and in a peacetime economy American chemical manufacturers were but very mildly interested in these markets and never have enjoyed, for one reason or another, the lion's share of any one of them. In fact, in any discussion of this subject it is only fair to point out that in peacetime not more than 10 percent of the total production of American chemicals went into export markets, as contrasted with between 40 and 60 percent in England and Germany. Our industry, now called upon to supply all the democracies, was normally geared for domestic consumption alone.

It is totally unfair to blame any one or any group for a shortage of certain chemicals. All evidence points to the fact that the War Department, in twenty years of planning for "M" Day, did not even remotely visualize a chain of circumstances such as the sudden and complete collapse of France and the Low Countries in a period of forty days; the passage of the Lend-Lease Bill; the switch on the part of Russia from the role of a passive partner of Germany to that of an active ally of Great Britain and the United States; the sudden and unprovoked attack of Japan upon the United States; the debacle at Pearl Harbor; the loss of the Philippines; and the fall of Malaya and Singapore. America's blueprint for war of but two years ago might well now be likened to the plans of a one-room squatter's shack when what is desperately needed is a hundred-story skyscraper. But the plans for what Donald M. Nelson, Chief of the War Production Board, has so aptly described as the "greatest production job in all history" are off the drafting boards and are being rapidly transformed into factories and actual sinews of war.

If the reader has received the impression from these pages that America's war effort has been dangerously hampered because of shortages of chemicals, the impression is an erroneous one. Serious shortages in a few products have developed, it is true, but they are notable because their number has been so relatively few, and indeed they are notable largely because they have existed at all. And even where shortages have arisen unexpectedly, prompt action by governmental agencies and intelligent cooperation on the part of the industry have made it possible to shift supplies to those industries where they would do the most good in the war effort. Fortunately for the success of that war effort the situation in 1942 in chemicals is quite different from that which prevailed in 1914.

The popular belief in many laymen's minds that the United States did not possess a chemical industry worthy of the name prior to 1914 is, of course, incorrect. We did produce in fairly large quantities a number of basic industrial chemicals, such as sulfuric acid, nitric acid, muriatic acid, sodium bichromate, and the alkalies which include soda ash, caustic soda and sodium bicarbonate.

America was, however, completely dependent at the outbreak of World War I on outside sources for potash and nitrates. It was almost wholly dependent upon imports for supplies of important intermediates, phenol, dyes, synthetic medicinals and pharmaceuticals, all derived from coal-tar crudes.

At the outbreak of the 1914 holocaust the United States produced less than 10 percent of the dyes it consumed and even that meager proportion was made from imported intermediates. By contrast, in 1940 the American dye industry produced about 95 percent of our total domestic consumption, and had an export balance of some 25,000,000 pounds.

We not only were woefully weak in 1914 in supplies of certain vital chemicals, but we were also lacking, in many instances, the actual technical knowledge required to produce these materials in sizable quantities. We were further vulnerable because the number of highly trained competent chemists and chemical engineers was small. Fortunately those we did have proved thoroughly capable of pioneering and the superhuman efforts of a comparatively small band of trained personnel turned the tide in a relatively short time and assured the United States a well-rounded and completely self-sustained chemical industry. The wisdom displayed by the late President Wilson and Congress in treating the chemical industry as a defense industry is now very apparent when the struggle of the democracies of the world to survive is largely dependent upon the productive capacity of the American chemical industry and the ingenuity of its chemists and engineers to expand its capacity still further in a very short time.

The 1914 bottleneck in chemicals, in brief, then, was directly caused by the British blockade and the inability of Germany to continue to send her supplies to this country. The bottleneck in 1942 is largely the result of a tremendous flow of exports to our Allies—either directly in the form of chemicals as such, or in finished goods which require large quantities of chemicals in processing operations. There is but one answer to this bottleneck—greater and ever greater productive capacities.

While this expansion is being made, however, and probably until Germany, Japan and their lesser allies are defeated, America must certainly "chemicalwise" pull in the belt several more notches. Non-defense industries consuming chemicals are finding it increasingly more difficult to obtain sufficient supplies, and the situation will become progressively worse.

Every Mr. and Mrs. John Q. Public have now become suddenly conscious of shortages of chemicals and question why they exist. Mr. Public has already discovered that it is difficult to obtain his favorite antifreeze for his automobile, that his dry-cleaner does not in all cases effectively remove the evidence from his vest of a particularly luscious meal; Mrs. Public is complaining to the laundryman that her wash when returned has definite signs of "tattle-tale gray," and is greatly disturbed about future availability of "silk" hose. Of course, Mr.

Public and Mrs. Public and all the little Publics are now tremendously worried about the rubber shortage, and how long the family jallopy will be able to operate on its "threadbare" rubber tires.

Has the American public suddenly become chemical-conscious? Decidedly so! And why? Because Mr. and Mrs. John Q. Public can't readily get many of the products and many of the normal services that help to make living in a free and prosperous nation worth while. And, too, Mr. and Mrs. John Q. Public had been led to believe that those queer fellows, the chemists, are miracle-makers; and certainly at this time a great many miracles are in order, or at least would solve a great many of our immediately pressing field problems.

Today the American chemical industry is experiencing war regimentation to a degree greater than that felt by any other single industry, with the notable exceptions of the automotive, rubber and steel.

This condition is not a totally unexpected one when it is realized that modern warfare is industrial warfare, and that the chemical industry not only supplies many of the direct implements of human and property destruction, but is a basic source of material for practically every other industrial manufacturing operation in peace or war.

One needs only to check the ever-increasing list of chemicals now under direct control, or to compare the War Department's list of critical and strategic materials published a little more than a year and a half ago with the present group of chemicals, metals, minerals and ores now under full mandatory priority, allocation, and/or price ceilings, fully to comprehend the serious degree of change that war has brought to the American chemical industry. Even the American lay public begins to comprehend to some degree the full significance of the revision of plans for increased productive capacities when it is revealed, for example, that the output of metallic magnesium is to be increased 3,900 percent, or from 10,000,000 pounds to 400,000,000 pounds annually, and this may not prove sufficient and the figure now aimed at is 700,000,000 pounds; that aluminum production must be raised from 400,000,000 pounds to one and one-half billion pounds, and possibly over two billion pounds; that toluol output, one of the vital ingredients in the manufacture of the explosive trinitrotoluene, must be increased from 25,000,000 gallons annually to well over 150,-000,000 gallons, and that practically all of this increase must come from an entirely new source—petroleum—rather than from by-product coking operations, or that production of industrial alcohol must be expanded four or five-fold, or from 100,000,000 gallons to possibly 500,000,000 gallons or more.

One can more easily visualize the problem facing the American chemical manufacturer today if a few of the outstanding examples of serious bottlenecks are reviewed. It is well to bear in mind in making such analyses that the chemical industry is a highly complex industry. There are numerous instances where a shortage of even a relatively small amount of one key material may be the complete bottleneck of the output of millions of pounds of other essential chemicals.

Chlorine is perhaps one of the most outstanding examples of chemical shortages, yet it seems but yesterday that one of the most serious and pressing problems confronting alkali manufacturers was the development of additional outlets of consumption to take care of a surplus of chlorine production. What has caused this reversal? There are several factors, among which are (1) the large quantities of chlorine necessary in the manufacture of polyvinyl chloride, which in turn is the basis for the manufacture of insulating material used in the Degaussing cables (magnetic mine belts on ships); (2) withdrawal of large quantities of chlorine from non-defense industries for the purpose of bleaching cotton linters utilized in the manufacture of high explosives; (3) need for relatively large quantities of chlorine for water purification purposes in army cantonments, new defense housing areas, etc.; (4) unrevealed, but certainly large quantities of chlorine withdrawn from industry for the manufacture of poison gases which may never be used, but which must be produced so that the threat of reprisal is ever present.

It is now conservatively estimated that well over one-half of the present increased production of chlorine is going into the manufacture of war material. Small wonder, then, that the paper industry (which is the largest single peacetime consumer of chlorine), the producers of ethylene glycol type of antifreeze, the manufacturers of liquid bleach necessary in laundry operations, and the producers of dry-cleaning compounds, are being restricted to smaller quantities of chlorine.

Chlorine was one of the first chemicals to receive attention from the former Office of Production Management. As early as July 26, 1941, full priority control was established, and four days later the OPA listed seven essential public services and industries which were to receive first civilian preference.

Methanol is also interesting from the price angle. Prior to 1926 all methanol produced in this country was made by the destructive wood distillation process. With the introduction of synthetic methanol prices gradually declined and in time most, if not all, of the wood distillers were forced out of the picture. Many of the plants were virtually abandoned. Now they are being brought back into production, even though their total output is but a fraction of our total requirements, but it is necessary to permit wood distillers to obtain higher prices for natural methanol than that allowed for synthetic! Nor is this just an isolated case. There are two sets of prices for industrial alcohol based upon what raw material is used. The emphasis is on production, regardless of cost.

The situation in explosives is an interesting study. The United States—peace-loving nation, with no ax to grind—had no particular incentive nor felt it necessary to erect tremendous explosive-producing units, until the Axis threat of world domination became unmistakably clear. Companies who were explosive manufacturers in World War I found it highly desirable later to diversify manufacturing interests and to produce products with large peacetime consumer appeal. The requirements of government, industry and sportsmen for explosives was relatively small and not particularly lucrative. But, with the advent of war it became very evident that the explosive industry in the United States must be expanded many times over, and that this production program must be carried out with Government funds and with tremendous speed so that the United States and other democracies of the world would be in a position to match the Axis program.

The explosive industry requires as basic materials toluol, phenol, alcohol and ammonia, as well as tremendous quantities of purified cellulose, the latter produced either from cotton linters or wood pulp. To obtain the necessary increase in toluol, chemists have turned to the almost inexhaustible supply of petroleum, and several plants are either in actual operation manufacturing enormous quantities of toluol, or will be on large-schedule production very shortly.

The situation in industrial alcohol recently became so critical that it was found necessary by the Office of Production Management early in January 1942 to require a large part of the whiskey distiller capacity of this country to be turned over into the production of industrial alcohol, using corn as the raw material. In this manner it is hoped to reach a production of some 400,000,000 gallons annually.

Again we see a striking example of how war disturbs the peacetime economic structure. Costs become entirely secondary, and the only question that does receive consideration is how quickly and how much of a given product can be made.

While the general subject of rubber is treated in detail elsewhere, it is important to point out that the Japanese attack on Pearl Harbor and the loss of Malaya have definitely made rubber a "problem child" of the chemical industry. While conservation of existing stocks on hand and greater reclaiming of rubber will prevent serious shortages for our military machine, the outlook is not a particularly bright one for civilian supplies for several years. It is now quite apparent that if America is to travel on wheels the chemical industry must provide that means, and that in the future rubber will largely be considered a chemical and not a natural raw material. Thus the chemical industry primarily is charged with the problem of developing what is practically an entirely new industry to America, and to do this in a period when construction costs are high and materials of construction and technical skill are scarce.

As we have seen in example after example of both natural raw materials and chemicals, modern war completely upsets the normal economic structure and industrial life of nations, creating, in many instances, demands for certain materials greatly in excess of any peacetime requirements. Without much question, the most striking example of this in World War II is magnesium.

For years, indeed ever since the close of the last war, Dow Chemical Company struggled to develop peacetime uses for magnesium, lightest of metals but very difficult to alloy or fabricate without employing very special technique. So great were the difficulties encountered that all of the producers of magnesium during World War I gradually gave up the ghost in the succeeding years and in time Dow alone survived in the field of metallic magnesium production.

In some years this company produced greatly in excess of the amount that could be marketed, in the hope that industry would finally grasp the full significance of what the metal offered. Year by year modest gains were recorded, and in the late Thirties consumption reached the sizable figure of some 6,000,000 pounds annually. And then came war in Europe and the belated discovery by the Allies that Germany was employing magnesium in a major way in the production of airplanes. And overnight a productive capacity of even 10,000,000 pounds annually looked hopelessly inadequate.

Fortunately, Dow Chemical, anticipating far greater consumption of this light metal, decided early in 1939 not only to increase productive capacity at its plant at Midland, Michigan, but to erect a plant at Freeport, Texas, to extract the metal from seawater. This forward-looking decision provided a much wider base for the Government to create a magnesium expansion program which calls for a forty-fold increase by the end of 1943.

One begins really to visualize the extent of the Government program on magnesium when the following figures are considered: Dow Chemical's production at Midland is now 18,000,000 pounds, and a somewhat similar quantity at Freeport. In the course of construction by Dow at Freeport and in conjunction with the Defense Plant Corporation (United States Government) is another 18,000,000 pound unit; and contracts were signed at the close of 1941 for still further additions at Freeport, amounting to 72,000,000 pounds, bringing the grand total for Dow alone to 126,000,000 pounds annually.

Plans of the Government magnesium program include some 48,000,-000 pounds to be produced by the Kaiser Ship Building interest, with plants at Permanente, California, and Spokane, Washington; the Basic Magnesium Inc., with a plant being erected at Las Vegas, Nevada, with an estimated output of 112,000,000 pounds annually.

Two of the alkali companies, Mathieson Alkali Works and Diamond Alkali Company, are each expected to bring into production some 36,000,000 pounds annually, at plants at Lake Charles, Louisiana, and Painesville, Ohio. International Agricultural Chemical, now known by its new official corporate name, the International Minerals & Chemical Corporation, has been asked by the Government to produce 24,000,000 pounds a year at Austin, Texas.

Production as outlined amounts to the astronomical figure of 382,-000,000 pounds, and additional negotiations are still under way to increase still further the magnesium expansion program to at least 400,000,000 pounds or more.

To increase further our magnesium supply a number of plants are being erected in various sections of the country based on the utilization of the Pidgeon development, a new ferrosilicon process developed by L. M. Pidgeon of the Canadian National Research Council. Ferrosilicon is used to reduce high-grade calcined dolomite to free magnesium which is then distilled from the reacting mass.

One may well ask is magnesium a metal or a chemical? While both chemists and metallurgists will agree that fundamentally, of course, it is a metal, methods for its production are all chemical. Therefore the magnesium program is largely, if not wholly, on the doorstep of the American chemical industry, and for this reason it is properly included in a discussion of chemicals.

The special emphasis which has been placed on the serious shortages of such products as chlorine, methanol, alcohol, certain other solvents and chemicals is likely to create the impression that serious shortages exist in the entire line of industrial chemicals, dyes, intermediates, pharmaceuticals and drugs. At the risk of repeating unnecessarily, it is well again to emphasize that, while certainly there have been no surpluses, in the main, American chemical manufacturers have been able adequately to take care of the reasonable needs of industry.

If one examines the list of chemicals under close War Production Board scrutiny and Government regulation, it is immediately seen that the number is not particularly large. Among the products for which price schedules were set before the general price ceiling orders were issued were formaldehyde, ethyl alcohol, acetic acid, wood alcohol, acetone, normal butyl alcohol and glycerine (as of January 12, 1942). Among the chemicals in the Voluntary Price Ceiling lists were ammonium sulfate, certain of the more important solvents, dry colors, zinc oxide, sulfuric acid, carbon black, bleaching powder, pyrophosphate and titanium pigments. It is necessary to point out, however, in connection with both formal and voluntary price ceilings, that a number of the metals were included, and such inclusion did have distinct bearing on the price schedules of their salts and derivatives.

Under the stress and strain of an all-out war program, the price structure in chemicals remained remarkably stable and unchanged. This is in direct contrast to the chaotic conditions which featured World War I. We have witnessed so far at least no spiral of constantly ascending prices such as caused terrific havoc, dislocation, disruption and serious interference with manufacturing operations twenty-five years ago. To the everlasting credit of the American chemical manufacturers, they have held down the price structure as close to the pre-defense period era as possible under very unfavorable circumstances, before price ceilings were established.

It would be untrue, of course, to state that there was no speculation in chemicals. There was a certain amount of speculation, but the volume of chemicals sold at high resale prices was very small in comparison with the total volume of production of American chemical manufacturers.

The American chemical industry was profoundly affected by World War I. It is reasonable to suppose that World War II likewise will have tremendous repercussions, both favorable and unfavorable.

No one can dispute the fact that World War I made possible many technological developments, abroad and in this country, and it is reasonable to suppose that the present international conflict will have similar effect, only more pronounced and profound, because the tempo of industrialization of industry and war has been stepped up tremendously in two decades. Very likely all of the scientific achievements of the 1914-1918 period would have been achieved in time in this country, even if the hand of Mars had been stayed a quarter of a century ago, but no one will dispute the fact that the war did accelerate the growth of the American chemical industry.

No reasonable person will mistake these words for either a direct or an indirect plea for war to subsidize research or to provide the impetus for accelerating scientific and industrial progress.

But we should not imitate the ostrich, with our heads in the sand, but rather should readily recognize and appreciate the fact that the present situation will bring about important changes, and that such changes and innovations will take place with a suddenness that will be startling and almost unbelievable.

It is well to remember that during the present emergency, peacetime economics are now largely, if not wholly, "out the window." Processes are being tried, developed and utilized without prime consideration as to relative costs. This in itself means much in accelerating the pace of development work in the primary or early stages. We are spending millions for synthetic rubber plants. Would this be happening were we not faced with a definite rubber shortage now?

Synthetic fibers—rayons, nylon, casein wool, and others—are unquestionably in for a period of sudden expansion as a result of the war with Japan in the Pacific.

The American tax payer is "footing" the greatest research expenditure that the world has ever witnessed. The national defense program of 1940 and 1941 and now the all-out war program are responsible for an increase of astronomical proportions in the productive capacity for nitrogen fixation, explosives, toluol, chlorine, synthetic resins, plastics, solvents of various kinds, including tremendous quantities of ethyl alcohol, and, of course, the metals, particularly the light metals—magnesium and aluminum. Such an expansion program can only result in startling innovations when the emergency is over.

While the expansion in aluminum and magnesium productive capacity is highly spectacular, such situations are not by any means confined to a relatively few materials. There are many others. The American chemical industry will find itself at the end of this war with both tremendous quantities of raw materials on hand and excess plant capacity to make more. This is a challenge, however, that the technologists in industry will meet successfully. New and unexpected uses will be found for magnesium, aluminum, solvents, ethyl alcohol, ammonia, methanol, formaldehyde, and a host of other metals and chemicals that are now being produced in greater quantities because they are prime essentials in industrial warfare.

One very obvious repercussion of the present emergency is likely to be a greatly accelerated expansion in the output of industrial chemicals derived from natural gas and petroleum. At the moment we are turning to natural gas and the petroleum industries as a source of raw materials for additional supplies of methanol, formaldehyde, synthetic alcohols, ammonia, and synthetic rubber.

Locked up in the petroleum reserves of the world is a great store-house of various chemicals. That these will become readily available is now a foregone conclusion, and more and more the petroleum industry will become chemical in nature.

Certainly, one of the most profound changes that has taken place as a result of our war program is the stimulation being given to the industrialization of the Pacific Northwest, the Boulder Dam area, and the Tennessee Valley, and to a slightly less extent the Midwest and Southwest. Hydroelectric power such as is now becoming available in ever-increasing quantities in the Pacific Northwest and the Boulder Dam area, attracts metallurgical and chemical production, for many of the operations in these two industries require steady sources of cheap power.

The difficulty experienced by the Department of the Interior in finding industries for the areas in which tremendous hydroelectric power developments have been created in the past five years, has been suddenly solved by a war program. There is actually a wait-ing-list, where a year or two ago there seemed little likelihood of

Chemicals under Government Control
(*As of Feb. 13, 1942*)

	Priority	Allocation	Price Control
Acetic Acid			x
Acetone			x
Ascorbic Acid			x
			(under consideration)
Aspirin			x
Bleaching Powder			x
Borax, Boric Acid	x		
Caffeine			x
			(under consideration)
Carbon Tetrachloride			x
Cellophane	x		
Chlorinated Rubber	x	x	
Chlorinated Solvents	x		
Chlorine	x		
Citric Acid			x
			(under consideration)
Ethyl Alcohol	x		x
Formaldehyde	x		x
Glycerine			x
Hexamethylenetetramine			x
Lithopone			x
Methanol	x		
Mercury	x		x
Neoprene	x	x	
Oxalic Acid			x
Paraformaldehyde	x		x
Phenols	x		
Phosphates (Triphenyl and Tricresyl)	x		
Phosphorus Oxychloride	x		
Polyvinyl Chloride	x		
Potassium Perchlorate	x		
Potassium Permanganate	x		
Refrigerant Gases	x	x	x
Rubber	x	x	
Sodium Nitrate		x	
Synthetic Resins	x		
Synthetic Rubber	x		
Toluene	x	x	
Tungsten and Compounds	x		

attracting industrial operations on a large scale for many years to come.

Unquestionably the establishment of these new industrial areas will dislocate to some degree the established economic structure of other sections of the country; it will create new transportation problems; it will disrupt present markets, and will lead ultimately to the establishment of several new ones. As the chemical industry serves practically all industries, it will feel these changes and be affected materially by them. Just how, cannot be determined with any degree of accuracy today.

No one, of course, has all of the answers, for no one knows how long the present emergency will continue, nor to what extent our present admittedly large expansion program will be further accelerated. It is but natural that American chemical management is speculating and is wondering what is to become of our expanded productive capacity, once the emergency is over. Will such plants be placed in a standby condition; will they be turned over to the companies who are now operating them for the Government; will they be sold to newcomers in the field; or will they be operated directly by the Government and in direct competition with private industries? He who could answer correctly all these questions now would indeed be a soothsayer of the first order.

Should the present emergency end suddenly, it is more than likely that we would duplicate the same situation that prevailed after the armistice in 1918—a war-swollen oversupply of practically every material produced.

It is at this point that American chemical research ingenuity must save the day by developing entirely new uses, or expanding existing uses for many of our consumer goods.

Despite the present all-out production effort, and emphasis on production, American chemical companies are showing care and foresight in maintaining as far as possible intensive research programs, in the hope and anticipation that new uses discovered in the next few years will require at least a large part of the increased productive capacity now being made available in the war program.

While 400,000,000 pounds of magnesium is a startling figure to contemplate, it is not beyond the realm of imagination to conceive that ultimately our requirements of this material may well exceed such a figure. The airplane industry, emulating the example of the automobile industry and its highly successful production methods, may very well make necessary still further peacetime increases in the productive capacities of our magnesium plants. Totally unexpected and yet unheard-of applications of this material may change a situation that now has all the earmarks of great uncertainty to one of tremendous optimism.

It is well to recall that after World War I our productive capacities in caustic soda and phenol appeared to be hopeless situations for the manufacturers of these products. Yet within a few years a rayon industry and a new plastic industry demanded such huge quantities of these chemicals that additional plant capacity was the only possible answer. Little did anyone visualize in 1920 three major alkali plants in the Southwest by 1936; nor could the phenol producers in 1920 picture a situation in 1942 when a large percentage of our production of that material would be moving to Russia under Lend-Lease.

The chemical industry is based on change. Changes from one product to another—from one process to another. All that we can be certain of is that there will be changes, profound technological changes.

The period ahead of us will be a great challenge to the scientific ingenuity and ability of our best scientific minds in the chemical field. It will also be a challenge to the business acumen of the industrial leaders of our great chemical-producing companies. It will call as never before for closely coordinated cooperation between the technical and commercial divisions of the chemical industry. Then, more than ever before, long-range planning will be vital, even though management will be called upon to steer a course through turbulent and largely uncharted seas.

Fats, Oils and Gums

Soldiers, statesmen, politicians, economists and writers have in twenty-odd years penned tons of explanations as to the whys and wherefores of Germany's ultimate collapse in the First World War. But the most direct cause (seldom mentioned) was a hopeless deficiency in fats and oils. Lack of these vital foods led to weakness, and weakness to the despair which hastened the defeat of the German people.

Strangely enough the fats and oils, the "Cinderellas" in the raw materials war-setup, do have an importance far greater than generally suspected by the public, and this despite the fact that the physical and mental well-being of every single man, woman and child depends upon the continued maintenance of large supplies. And it is equally true that the fats and oils are vital to industry. John Q. Public and even the "Quiz Kids" probably can without much hesitation tell you all about nylon, or synthetic rubber, or nitrates, but it is doubtful whether the names tung, perilla and oiticica would mean very much to them.

For the last two decades tung, or Chinawood oil, has been used extensively in formulating fast-drying paints. There was a time when only tung and perilla oil, also from China, were available as important drying oils, other than, of course, linseed which from a tonnage point of view was and still is the most important. However, in the last five or six years oiticica, from Brazil, has come forward to help us replace the Far Eastern product. We have also started in a modest way our own plantations of tung oil in the Gulf Coast region.

Official estimates of America's consumption of these vital commodities place 1941 figures at somewhere near eleven billion pounds. This is an indicated gain of over 10 percent over the 1940 total of nearly ten billion pounds, which was an all-time record. The outlook for 1942 indicates a further increase in demand of possibly another two billion pounds—and this in face of the fact that war in the Pacific practically cuts us off from 15 percent of our supplies, principally cocoanut oil, palm oil and tung oil.

There are twelve oils that we normally import in sizable quantities —they account for 95 percent of our imports. The leading supplying countries in terms of weight of the oil or oil equivalent were, in 1940: The Philippines, which supplied 45 percent of the total; Netherlands Indies, 13 percent; Argentina, 12 percent; Brazil, 10 percent; China, including Hong Kong, 6 percent. The Philippines normally supply us with cocoanut (partly as oil, and partly in the form of copra). From the Netherlands Indies comes palm oil; from Argentina linseed in the form of flaxseed; from Brazil castor-oil, babassu and oiticica; and from China, of course, comes Chinawood or tung oil.

To meet an expected increase of 10 to 15 percent in demand for fats and oils during the current year the Department of Agriculture has announced plans for an expansion of more than a billion pounds in the production of domestic vegetable oils. It has set the crop goal for peanuts at an increase of 255 percent over 1941; soybeans 154 percent; and flaxseed 134 percent. Additional measures are contemplated to bring about increased recovery of lard, tallow, and greases in packing plants and other establishments.

Admittedly the situation in fats and oils is serious as a result of increased civilian and defense requirements, coupled with the loss of imports from the Far East; but fortunately it is not critical and does not present the problems that do rubber and tin, for we can ultimately grow our full fats and oils requirements domestically if necessary and can even turn to that growing haven of chemical magic —the petroleum industry—for products that will serve in certain uses, particularly soap manufacture. Then, too, fats and oils technology has made some very remarkable gains in the last few years, making the substitution of one oil for another a much more practical procedure than in the past. And last, but certainly not of minor importance, are the long-term opportunities developing in South America, still more highly productive sources of drying oils.

But before we go any deeper into this intriguing story of fats and oils, let us consider certain of the fundamentals involved.

First, from the point of view of origin, fats and oils (other than petroleum) may roughly be said to be either vegetable, animal or fish derived. Second, oils and fats are divided into edible and inedible classifications. Oils are also divided into drying oils, semi-drying oils and non-drying oils. The paint, varnish, ink and linoleum manufacturers are the large consumers of the so-called drying oils, and the principal members of this group include tung oil, largely imported from China and now produced in relatively small quantities along the Gulf Coast; linseed oil, derived from flaxseed grown domestically and imported largely from Argentina and Canada; and to a less extent perilla, from China, oiticica from Brazil, and several fish oils processed along our eastern and western coasts.

It is as food that fats and oils are of greatest importance. Approximately 67 percent of the total consumption enters into food products, 20 percent into soap, 8 percent into paints, varnishes, etc., and 5 percent into miscellaneous products. Of the materials entering into food products, margarine alone accounted for over 23 percent of the total consumption of fats and oils entering all uses; and lard, which is mainly consumed as such in cooking and baking, accounted for nearly 20 percent of the total. Other oils and fats in the edible group are cottonseed oil (largely hydrogenated to become a substitute for lard and butter in cooking), soybean oil, corn oil, oleo oil, edible animal stearine, edible tallow and edible cocoanut oil. Domestic production accounted for 89 percent of the total of 6.3 billion pounds of all fats and oils entering edible uses in 1938 and for 96 percent of the total of 6.5 billions in 1940.

From the food viewpoint we should be able to solve any problem that arises. Certainly we will be able to provide amply for our own needs, and should be able to help our war partners substantially. All that we need do is to increase our acreages planted to cotton, soybeans, corn and peanuts, and increase our hog production. But like building Rome and like turning out ships, planes, tanks and guns, we cannot plant crops or double the pig population of the country in a day. Indeed, it is a much more difficult problem to rush Nature than it is to speed up the building of a city or a battleship.

It is when we move into the industrial uses of fats and oils that we begin to meet some extremely serious problems and for many reasons the soap industry presents quite a few difficulties.

The American public, firm in the belief that "cleanliness is next to godliness," has continued almost year after year to register new highs in soap consumption. In 1941 seventy-six manufacturers, representing 90 percent of the total production, sold $326,123,270 worth of soap, 25.8 percent more than in 1940. Liquid soaps were up 36.2 percent; other soap 18.6 percent.

And one by-product of the American fetish for personal cleanliness is glycerine, recovered in soap manufacture—an important ingredient in the production of explosives. And so when Johnny rather unwillingly washes his hands many, many more times a day than he, personally, sees any necessity for, he has unwittingly been helping to swell the output of glycerine to some 193,000,000 pounds (100 percent basis). Of this total approximately 75 percent went into war materials in the last twelve months.

The very vital importance of glycerine in war is sufficient reason to believe that despite a threatened shortage of fats and oils and more specifically of cocoanut oil and palm oil no attempt will be made by the War Production Board to restrict soap production. On the contrary, it is to be expected that every incentive will be given to the soap manufacturers to increase production still further, provided of course, glycerine is recovered. It is for this reason that home-manufacture of soap is frowned upon. So, too, is the soap producer who is not equipped to recover glycerine, or the "soaper" whose equipment does not permit full glycerine recovery. Those in these categories will be required to ship their materials to plants where efficient recovery operations are possible.

War does indeed create some very strange anomalies. Here and in Canada we will be strenuously urged on to even greater cleanliness in order to consume more soap, while our British brethren will be forced to cut their consumption some 20 percent. In England each person will be rationed every week to four ounces of household soap, three of toilet soap, three of flakes or chips, six or twelve of powder depending on its quality. By reducing the cleanliness of the British 20 percent, some 50,000 tons of valuable shipping space will be saved. The raw materials for soap manufacture are extremely bulky and the amount of glycerine our British allies will lose through reducing soap production we will more than make up here and will ship to them. Thus England's cleanliness may suffer but she will be none the less effective in an explosives sense.

Nor is this the end to the story of glycerine—a most interesting sidelight of the fats and oils industry. Glycerine can be produced by fermentation and from petroleum, but for several years the price has been rigidly held by the by-product producers to a level below the profitable range for producing it by either of these two methods. Hence the best we have so far is a pilot plant for making glycerine synthetically from petroleum.

It is interesting, however, to note that previous to the introduction of this process glycerine was one of the most speculative in the long list of raw materials, and prices literally "ran all over the lot." To date all that the synthetic process has obtained from a practical point of view is a "ceiling" on glycerine prices. And the recent confirmation (October, 1941) of this ceiling by the Office of Price Administration naturally did not provide incentive to any commercial introduction of either the synthetic or fermentation process on a large scale. We may yet come to the point where the output of glycerine as a by-product of soap manufacture may not be sufficient for our needs and those of our allies, and we may see plants erected with Government funds to make the product synthetically or by fermentation.

Unfortunately for glycerine, and unfortunately for the future quality of much of our soap output, the source of most of our cocoanut oil is the Philippines, now entirely cut off from us.

The glycerine content in cocoanut oil is very high when comparison is made with other oils. The gradual elimination of cocoanut oil, unless we can obtain it in sufficient quantity from Latin America and the West Indies, will mean a gradual lowering in the quality of our soaps; it will mean that most toilet and laundry soaps will not lather as well as formerly. It will probably mean a death blow to liquid soaps and shampoos, for about 90 percent of these are formulated with cocoanut oil.

There is no possibility of a soap shortage in 1942, but there is more than the possibility that quality may begin to decline. But that will not interfere with consumption, for soap in this country is one of the definite necessaries and not a luxury, and if we cannot get the quality to which we are accustomed we will take what we can get, will use it as freely and be thankful we have it.

It is the high lauric acid content of cocoanut oil and palm-kernel oil that gives to soaps made with them the very desirable free-lathering properties. It is for this very reason that "soapers" import annually some 400,000,000 pounds of lauric acid oils, about 25 percent of the total fats and oils employed in soap-making, and it is quite significant that a recent release of the United States Tariff Commission has this to say: "No fat or oil now produced or likely to be produced in any appreciable quantity in the United States contains lauric acid."

It has been demonstrated that soaps made from oleic and palmitic acids are equal in cleansing properties to those made from oils high in lauric acid content, but it is necessary that the large quantities of stearic acid be removed or separated from the oleic and palmitic acids. Right here comes in that very important item, namely equipment. We know all about the technology of many things, such as synthetic rubber, synthetic glycerine, a synthetic cocoanut oil or lauric acid—but which should be given preference in the allocation of equipment. Frankly, it is not within the province of the authors of this book to say.

Fortunately not all the fats and oils consumed in soap manufacture present the problem that we face in the matter of lauric acid oils. Total fats and oils consumption in the soap industry in 1940 totaled 1.7 billion pounds. Animal fats and oils supplied a greater proportion of the total than vegetable oils in all the years between 1930 and 1940. It must be remembered that the "soaper" does have some leeway in the selection of the fats and oils he employs in formulation.

Probably in no other industry are relative prices of commodities watched so closely in normal times. The economist in this industry shares with the chemist and practical soap-maker a voice in what ingredients find their way into the soap kettle. Now a new voice will be heard—that of the Government—to tell us what is available, what must be used to secure the highest yield of a sorely needed by-product. War regimentation has now reached the cake of soap in your bathroom and the margarine in the refrigerator. In the formulation of both, Government agencies will have the last word in order to obtain a maximum of glycerine production. In margarine production emphasis will be put on reducing the edible cocoanut oil content in favor of cottonseed and animal oils.

It would be encouraging to turn to the position of the drying oils (used in coatings) if the existing situation were an improvement over the problems now confronting the "soaper," but frankly the varnish kettle presents no improvement in this respect over the soap kettle. In one way at least, however, the coatings manufacturer has had quite an advantage over the soap-maker—a little more time to prepare; for the Japanese-Chinese War of the last four years has given us a chance to experience just what it means to face an ever-declining volume of supplies of tung and perilla oils. It has provided paint technologists with a period of grace in which to alter formulations, and to the everlasting credit of the chemists of the coatings field they have, in many instances, not only solved problems of shortages but actually improved products as a direct result of such wartime stimulation.

Total consumption of fats and oils in the manufacture of paints, varnishes, linoleum, and printing inks in 1940 totaled 796,000,000 pounds. Of this total, paints and varnishes accounted for $83\frac{1}{2}$ percent, linoleum and oilcloth for 14 percent and printing inks for $2\frac{1}{2}$ percent. Linseed accounts for between two-thirds and three-fourths of the total annual consumption.

War in the East has played some devastating tricks on normal consumption of drying oils. For example, tung oil in the past decade has accounted for between 13 and 20 percent of the total; yet in 1940 it dropped to $8\frac{1}{2}$ percent; in 1941 it was even less, and the outlook for 1942 is for still greater restriction. Indeed, with shipments from China now at an end, allocation of the fast-dwindling stocks has become absolutely necessary.

The effect of Japan's attack on China is seen in a comparison of 1937 and 1940 figures for the consumption of imported drying oils. The imported oils (including those made here from imported materials) accounted for 80 percent of the total in 1937, but for only 44 percent in 1940. In the interval consumption of soybean, castor, oiticica, and fish oils has increased. Improvements in formulation, including much wider use of synthetic resins, have assisted in meeting these abnormal conditions.

For years the technology of the fats and oils failed to receive the attention its importance really warranted. Soap-making, one of the earliest of arts, continued in this stage for centuries; and much the same criticism can be leveled at the paint and varnish industries. But it is a trite but nevertheless true statement that "necessity is the mother of invention." The technological advances in both the soap and coatings fields in the past decade have probably surpassed all the improvements of the preceding half-century.

We have learned, for example, to improve the drying qualities of what were formerly classified as semi-drying oils. Who would have suspected five years ago that in 1941 we would be completing a commercial installation capable of producing at least 30,000,000 pounds of quick-drying oils by a process of fractionation and using semi-drying oils as the raw material? How widely is it known that at least two well-known research groups are feverishly working on selective solvent extraction processes for turning out satisfactory drying oils from semi-drying oils? And that irrepressible petroleum industry may have at least a partial answer to our need for drying oils with a by-product made by extracting and polymerizing what is known to the chemist as an intermediate olefin. And what is perhaps the most spectacular development of them all, in fats and oils technology in 1941, was the use of frozen lard as a refrigerant in the transatlantic shipment of meat to Britain.

On the favorable side is the steady increase in the availability of dehydrated castor-oil for use as a drying oil. There is the most encouraging picture of large stocks of flaxseed (raw material for linseed oil) both here and in Canada and in Argentina. Our own domestic production of tung or Chinawood oil is increasing year by year and the quality is generally excellent and much more uniform than that coming from China. Higher prices will stimulate South American production of castor beans, babassu nuts and oiticica nuts. For the first time, a domestic production of castor beans will be available in 1942.

In any attempt at reaching conclusions about 1942 requirements of drying oils it is well to remember that automobile production has been discontinued for the duration and the same is true of home construction except in newly settled defense production areas. Therefore during the remainder of 1942 and 1943 we probably will not see any great increase over 1941's record consumption, despite the fact that we will soon be nearing the peak of a war production program.

Indeed, we are learning much and learning it fast under the stimulus of war. For years it has been commonly believed that large quantities of imported palm oil (largely from the Netherlands Indies) were absolutely necessary in the manufacture of tin plate. The present outlook for tin plate is hardly conducive to any bullish sentiment over the volume of consumption of palm oil for this particular use. But we will have some tin and there is a very strong possibility that hydrogenated cottonseed oil or hydrogenated peanut oil may prove to be a perfectly satisfactory substitute.

In general, stocks of fats and oils were considered to be particularly large at the end of 1941—a favorable position for us, since it is likely to be some time before we again have free access to the four corners of the earth. It is not unlikely, either, that large buyers of imported oils have been preparing for the eventuality that finally caught up with us on December 7. We do know that stocks of animal fats and greases—particularly butter, lard, and inedible tallow—reached a new high of 615,000,000 pounds at the end of September, 1941.

The Office of Price Administration has moved quickly and so far at least effectively against speculation and hoarding. Export control was placed in effect in April, 1941. A few days after the Japanese attack on Pearl Harbor price ceilings were announced on fats and oils. Within a few weeks the OPA raised the ceilings 11 percent and the then Office of Production Management temporarily limited inventories to a 90-day period.

But there is also another side to the price story. Prices are now 25 percent above the 1927-1929 price level—they increased nearly 75 percent in the past year, caused principally by restricted availability of ocean shipping, increased exports, enlarged domestic demand and inventory purchasing in expectation of higher prices and possibly through fear that war might come in the Pacific.

Prices of fats and oils may very likely average higher in 1942 than in 1941, but it is fully expected that advances from the December (1941) level will be limited by control measures.

Ceilings on wholesale prices of fats and oils (excluding butter) are now set at the October 1, 1941, level or at 111 percent of the November 26, 1941, level, whichever was higher, with the special provision that the ceilings for soybean oil and linseed oil will be the October 1 price plus 0.75 percent per pound.

Present ceiling prices, however, are considerably below prices during and immediately following the First World War.

To summarize, we find that the position of the United States and the United Nations in fats and oils, while not critical, is studded with a number of question-marks. The situation, while not as critical as those which prevail in rubber and certain of the metals, is indeed serious. Drives will be made to enlist the housewives of America to save grease so that we will be certain to have sufficient quantities of glycerine. The butcher will be instructed to trim meats to a much greater degree and the meat packers will be called upon to do likewise. We have sufficient supplies if we only "husband" these carefully.

Much of what has been said about fats and oils applies equally to many of our natural gums and certain of our important waxes, notably Japan wax.

The impact of the Pacific war has had a direct effect, for example, on the gum copal supplies coming from the Netherlands Indies. Exports of gum copal to the United States have risen steadily for several years, growing from 4,049 metric tons in 1938 to 8,108 in 1940, and 1941 totals are reliably reported to be even higher. The United States was also, up to recently, taking about half of India's shellac exports. Already our phonographic record industry, large users of shellac, have found it necessary to offer to purchase old records which can be "reclaimed" as scrap quite similar to the practice of the rubber industry.

Certain gums, a few waxes and certain of the natural tanstuffs and dyestuffs are involved in this raw material picture as a result of the unexpected development of a major theatre of war in the Far East. They do not, however, present unsurmountable difficulties; provided of course, we hold, as the President in his February 23rd fireside chat suggested, to the role of eagles—not turtles.

[12]

Conclusion

THE outstanding conclusion to be drawn from the facts and figures presented in the foregoing pages is, of course, the indisputable fact that all of our tremendous natural wealth, stupendous though it be, is not sufficient to win a decisive victory in this war unless greatly augmented by tapping new sources of supplies. We produce in larger quantities more of the essential raw materials needed in this world-wide struggle than any other nation—yet we must import or produce synthetically several of the most vital sinews of war. Outstanding in this group of "must" raw materials are tin and rubber, but these by no means constitute the entire list of products that have become "problem children" in this most industrialized of all wars. Our problems of World War I were merely "child's play" when comparison is made with those we face in World War II and which must be solved if we are to maintain the American way of life inviolate. America must win, America will win but only by toil, sweat, blood and tears—and a high degree of technological ingenuity the like of which the world has never before witnessed. In World War I we had virtual control of the seven seas and the active cooperation of the navies of France, Italy and Japan. Today the remnants of the French navy are still a definite threat and the naval power of Japan and Italy, combined with a much more efficient German submarine force, constitute a powerful threat to our lifelines.

American industry has performed the impossible! When the full story of what has been accomplished can be told it will be the most amazing miracle of the twentieth century, for although America was the most industrialized nation on the face of this earth it was geared almost wholly to peacetime pursuits, to raising still higher the standard of living of the masses—not to destroying mankind.

218

Literally we still do not have a complete understanding of what the word "conversion" really means. We have been too close to the forest to see the trees. But on the battle lines scattered over the four corners of the globe the products of our factories are beginning to force upon ruthless enemies the realization that America was really not "soft" but was rather unwilling to believe for a long time that in this day and age men could be so depraved as to force upon civilization a base prostitution of the scientific advances of the last few decades.

Yes, indeed, American industry, supposedly too absorbed with mere profits to be mindful of the welfare of America, has turned in a brilliant performance that can only be described as unmatched in the annals of American history. It is worth recording for posterity that in June 1940 when France fell under the German hordes the United States produced but $150,000,000 worth of war materials. A year later this comparative monthly figure had risen to $800,000,000. The month of Japan's infamous attack on Pearl Harbor also witnessed a rise in the monthly war expenditures of this nation to $1,800,000,000, an increase better than tenfold in eighteen months, and just five months later this figure reached the staggering total of $3,500,000,000, an increase of twenty-fold within the short space of twenty-four months. Already the combined output of the Allied Nations exceeds the 1941 output of Germany and at an ever increasing pace we are fast outstripping our enemies. In May of this year American War production passed the British output 50 days ahead of schedule and in 1943 it will definitely be at least three times that of the British. The significance of these figures becomes more apparent when it is stated that the 1941 war production of the Allied Nations, exclusive of the United States, equalled the total 1941 output of Germany.

Since Pearl Harbor the emphasis has been placed on production and mainly through conversion of existing plant and manufacturing facilities. Today the emphasis is decidedly on the maintenance of a steady and an ever-increasing flow of raw materials to feed the greatest production schedule ever devised by man. It will not be easy to do despite our enormous resources for we must face the stark realization that the President's statement that we are in truth "the arsenal of democracy" was indeed if anything an understatement of the actual conditions as they have developed in the past four months.

To date we have successfully diverted raw materials to the war production lines by the relatively simple expedient of curtailing consumption of vital raw materials in the manufacture of civilian goods. Such action on the part of the War Production Board has yet to be felt by the public at large but before the end of 1942 every one of the 130,-000,000 Americans, old and young alike, will be keenly conscious that America is in an all-out war effort. By December we will see the end of luxuries, indeed we will see the end of everything but the bare essentials of living. Among the standard American products that will be off the dealers' shelves will be automobiles, tires, electric refrigerators, washing machines, radios, vacuum cleaners, and other electrical devices, as well as canned goods, articles which use metal foil, plastics, and consumer goods containing steel, rubber, copper, tin, nickel, aluminum and other critical metals and materials. By December, if not sooner, Mr. and Mrs. John Q. Public may find that at least some fifteen items normally important in the "American way of life" will be severely rationed. But what, indeed, is such a sacrifice when compared with totalitarianism?

How is the American war production machine to be "fed" from here on to victory? Much of it must come from the scrap piles of America. We cannot have the proverbial "cake and eat it too." As of the first of the year we did possess sizable stockpiles of rubber, tin, manganese, fats and oils and other vital products. With production geared at such a terrific pace we must certainly have reduced considerably such stocks. We must turn then to imports from brand new sources of supply, synthetically produced materials, utilization of low grade ores and minerals which in peacetime were uneconomical to operate, and last but certainly not least in importance the waste materials of industry and the home-materials which we have scorned in the past but which now may well prove to be the slim margin between victory and defeat.

From American industry must come approximately 75 percent of the scrap materials and salvage that must be brought into play; the housewives must provide the balance.

As this is written the big push for scrap is on. Under the stimulus of a direct radio plea of the President America is hunting in cellars, attics and in barns for every single piece of old rubber than can be located. Government authorities estimate that some 300,000 to 500,000 tons of scrap rubber is collectible in this country aside from the 1,200,000 tons in tires now on the roads. But not all of this can be reclaimed for it is conservatively estimated that but 50 to 75 percent of the total can be expected to appear as reclaim. Yet what has been brought to the surface so far, assures our reclaiming industry at least a year's supply, for at the moment the capacity of such plants has been estimated at 320,000 long tons per year. Uncle Sam needs your rubber. A few ounces of rubber in a hot water bottle or a few pounds in a discarded hose when multiplied by millions create a great national stockpile of rubber that will help to keep automobiles and trucks moving on the home front and war equipment rolling on the war front.

What is true of rubber is likewise true of fats and oils for from that which ordinarily poured down the sinks of America must come much of the glycerine that is required to make the explosives that will drive Hitler and his satellites to cover.

You housewives—are you doing your bit to win this war? Every two pounds of waste fat that you collect will provide enough glycerine to fire five antitank gun shells. Each family is expected to collect between one and two pounds of fat a month. Give over a corner of your refrigerator to this precious collection can. Save every bit of fat and grease you can; place it in a flat top can and bring it to your butcher.

Save every scrap of rag, every tin can, every collapsible tube you open. While the lowly tin can contains but 1.5 per cent tin, upwards of 800,000 tons of tin cans can be collected in this country and not only tin but scrap steel can be salvaged that will make the day of reckoning for Messrs. Hitler, Mussolini and Hirohito just that much nearer.

Industry, appreciating the value of America's scrap pile, is actively cooperating in spreading the gospel of saving to win the war. Three mighty salvage campaigns have been inaugurated to pump rubber, ferrous and nonferrous metals, and fats and oils into a huge reservoir for reclamation. A general salvage venture, underwritten by the American Iron and Steel Institute, a special fats and oils drive, sponsored by the Glycerine and Associated Industries, and a rubber collection drive in which the Petroleum Industry War Council is actively cooperating, are the spearheads of a concerted industry effort to bring forth from the kitchens, attics and cellars of America the vital raw materials to keep American production rolling in high gear.

The chemists and engineers of America are playing a great part in finding ways and means of producing synthetically many of the raw materials formerly imported and the most notable, of course, is synthetic rubber. Yet these men cannot perform miracles by resorting to a little "hocus pocus" with test tubes. Before any chemical process can be used commercially long hours of laboratory research, months of pilot plant testing are necessary. The public is not, normally, conscious of these development stages; the lay public is usually presented only with the finished product. The man on the street subconsciously believes the chemist is some sort of a magician who by simply waving a wand causes rabbits to jump out of a hat. Little does he realize that in normal times as many as five to seven years elapse between the birth of an idea and its introduction on a full-scale commercial basis. John Q. Public finds the preliminary stages very tedious. But he must remember too, that besides having to check and double-check every experiment the chemist and the engineer must also have the necessary equipment to make his tests and the materials to build the factory and the large-scale equipment to produce the material in large volume. Shall we build ships or plants? Even a steel production in excess of 90,000,000 tons does not provide us with all the steel that is required to do the thousand and one things necessary in this stupendous war program.

Under the stimulus of stark necessity the chemist and the engineer are cutting corners in a manner that is even surprising the technically trained minds of the country. In a few months very much simpler and inexpensive means have been found to produce synthetic rubber and even entirely new techniques to produce both much needed 100-octane gasoline for military planes and butadiene for synthetic rubber have been announced by two companies—Standard Oil of New Jersey and the Houdry Process Corporation—while chemists of the Bureau of Standards have reported startling innovations in the processes for utilizing low grade ores and minerals.

Not alone do shortages exist in raw materials but also in the technical manpower to perform the miracles we ask for and, indeed, must have to triumph in the end. Again the lay public little realizes that America as large as she is does not have an unlimited supply of highly trained technologists. Indeed, the reservoir is tragically inadequate. The National Roster of chemists, engineers, physicists, bacteriologists, geologists, and the like in all fields of science carries but one-quarter of a million names—a total wholly insufficient to inaugurate and carry through successfully the programs now arranged unless we do conserve such manpower and utilize it to the fullest extent possible. These men are irreplaceable and upon the intelligent use of their peculiar

abilities may well depend the outcome of the war. The qualified chemist or engineer carrying a gun in this industrialized and chemicalized
war is helping not hindering Mr. Hitler. It is not a matter of patriotism
—in stark reality victory will rest with the side that can produce the
thousands of mechanized sinews of war in the greatest volume and in
the shortest possible space of time.

The scientific brains of this country must be conserved to develop
quickly ways and means of utilizing our sources and our Western
Hemisphere neighbors' sources of low grade ores that will provide us
with antimony, chrome, tungsten, manganese in tremendous quantities, replacing the supplies that we in normal times imported from
sources now cut off.

Indeed, without Canadian and Latin American resources we would,
in fact, be very much handicapped in this mad armament race and
the outlook would be very much clouded and uncertain for the
democracies.

Nickel, aluminum, platinum, asbestos, copper—all these materials
are coming in from our northern neighbor and ally and such shipments do not move through submarine infested sea-lanes. Particularly
as far as nickel is concerned we could not get along without Canadian
imports which furnish 85 percent of our needs, and there are no other
large sources in this hemisphere of asbestos. Very fortunate, indeed,
for us that Canada is both a good neighbor of long standing and an
active ally in the present struggle.

In Latin America—we have substantial existing sources of supply
and very much larger potential ones. Several of the minerals we need
for armament are now being imported from countries south of the
Rio Grande; much larger quantities will be received in the future
when transportation facilities have been increased and mining operations further developed. Just as important are the agricultural products we can import from our neighbors to the South. Rubber is the
one now in the limelight but it is by no means the only badly needed
material now available to us only in Latin America. Cinchona bark
from which quinine is made means as much as rubber to a soldier
fighting in the tropics and a kapok life preserver may spell the difference between life and death to the sailor whose boat is going down
under a U-boat attack. Argentine wool, too, and the tanning materials
from that part of the world play a large part in clothing both soldiers
and sailors, and sisal from Mexico is having to replace the Manila

hemp that we formerly imported from the Philippines to make marine cordage. These are but a few of the reasons why it is very important for us to have the entire Western Hemisphere actively on our side in this war.

And when the battle is over and victory is ours, the two American continents will be in a position to enjoy a prosperity such as the world has never known. Hemisphere autonomy developed by the emergency will have far-reaching results, not only on our own welfare, but on world wide trade and international economy.

We will no longer be wholly dependent on sources outside the Western Hemisphere for our tin, antimony, tungsten, rubber, cinchona bark, kapok, fats and oils. South America will no longer be quite so dependent on European markets since the United States will have become a highly profitable customer of Latin American products. The "Good Neighbor" policy, a valuable asset in the fight of democracy to survive, will then provide a shining example to a war-torn and war-weary world of how countries big and small can live together indefinitely in peace and harmony.